Buses

Restored 2001

Buses

Restored 2001

Compiled in association with the
National Association of Road Transport Museums

Ian Allan
PUBLISHING

Front cover: Salford City Transport 112, a 1962 Daimler CVG6 is part of the Manchester Museum of Transport Collection. *Philip Lamb*

Back cover: Lowestoft Corporation Transports No 22, a 1947 AEC Regent II is preserved as an exhibit at the East Anglia Transport Museum. *Philip Lamb*

Half title: Privately preserved vehicles often appear at museum open days. Here Sunbeam F4 of the Australian Tees-side Railless Traction Board makes an appearance at the East Anglia Transport Museum. Originating with Reading Corporation as No 186 it was repatriated for preservation. *Peter Waller*

Title page:
This 1964 Bristol FS6G, Crosville DFG157, passed out of service and straight into preservation, and now resides at St Helens Transport Museum.
Philip Lamb

First published 2001

ISBN 0 7110 2813 3

© Ian Allan Publishing Ltd 2001

Published by Ian Allan Publishing

an imprint of Ian Allan Publishing Ltd, Hersham, Surrey KT12 4RG.
Printed by Ian Allan Printing Ltd, Hersham, Surrey KT12 4RG.

Code: 0103/B2

Contents

Introduction	7
What is NARTM?	9
Preserving and Restoring a Bus	10
How to Use this Book	14

Part 1
Museums Normally open to the Public

Abbey Pumping Station, Leicester	18
Amberley Museum	18
Aston Manor Road Transport Museum	20
Birmingham & Midland Museum of Transport	22
Black Country Living Museum	26
Bristol Aero Collection	27
British Commercial Vehicle Museum, Leyland	28
Castle Point Transport Museum, Canvey Island	28
Cavan & Leitrim Railway, Dromod	30
City of Portsmouth Preserved Transport Depot	30
Cobham Bus Museum	32
Dover Transport Museum	35
East Anglia Transport Museum, Carlton Colville	35
Imperial War Museum, London	36
Ipswich Transport Museum	37
Isle of Wight Bus Museum	38
Keighley Bus Museum	39
Lincolnshire Road Transport Museum	41
London Transport Museum	42
Manchester Museum of Transport	43
Museum of British Road Transport, Coventry	47
Museum of Transport, Glasgow	47
National Museum of Science and Industry	48
North of England Open Air Museum, Beamish	49
Nottingham Transport Heritage Centre	50
Oxford Bus Museum	51
St Helens Transport Museum	52
Sandtoft Transport Centre	56
Scottish Vintage Bus Museum, Lathalmond	58
Sheffield Bus Museum	64
Tameside Transport Collection, Mossley	66
Transport Museum Society of Ireland, Howth	66
Ulster Folk & Transport Museum, Cultra	68
Wirral Transport Museum	69

Part 2
Other Collections of Preserved Buses & Coaches

Aldershot & District Bus Interest Group	72
Aycliffe & District Bus Preservation Society	74
Bolton Bus Group	74
Bournemouth Heritage Transport Collection	76
Bristol Vintage Bus Group	77
British Trolleybus Society	78
Cardiff & South Wales Trolleybus Project	78
Chelveston Preservation Society	79
Cherwell Bus Preservation Group	80
Chesterfield 123 Group	80
Devon General Society	82
Dewsbury Bus Museum	84
East Pennine Transport Group	85
Friends of King Alfred Buses	85
Glasgow Bus Museum	87
Golcar Transport Collection	87
Huddersfield Passenger Transport Group	88
Kelvin Amos Collection	89
Lancastrian Transport Trust	90
Legionnaire Group	91
Meltham Mills Bus Museum	91
Merseyside Transport Trust	92
Mike Sutcliffe Collection	93
North East Bus Preservation Society	93
Ribble Vehicle Preservation Trust	96
RTW Bus Group	97
SELNEC Preservation Society	99
Solent Transport Trust	99
Southdown Historic Vehicle group	99
Telford Bus Group	101
Three Counties Bus & Commercial Vehicle Museum	102
Wealdstone & District Vintage Vehicle Collection	102
West Country Historic Omnibus & Transport Trust	104
West Midlands Bus Preservation Society	104
West of England Transport Collection	106
Westgate Museum	107

Part 3
Heritage Bus Services

Blue Triangle	110
Carmel Coaches	111
Cosy Coaches	112
Cumbria Classic Coaches	113
Green Bus Service	114
Mac Tours	115
Memory Lane Travel	116
Nostalgiabus	117
Rexquote Heritage	118
Southcoast Motor Services	119
Index of Vehicles by Registration Number	**122**
Index of Museums, collections and Heritage Bus Services	**128**

Still in residence at its old garage, now St Helens Transport Museum is St Helens 260, one of a number of that undertaking's Marshall-bodied AEC Swifts in preservation. *Philip Lamb*

Introduction

Welcome to the second edition of *Buses Restored*. The first edition, published in 2000, listed well over 1.200 buses and coaches in preservation in the British Isles. As a result, other groups have contacted Ian Allan and NARTM and have asked to have their own collections included in the database while some groups have moved from Part 2 to Part 1 as their ambitions to allow the public to view their vehicles have come to fruition.

Quite a number of buses have moved in, out and between collections and we will leave it to the avid reader to spot the changes! Others have joined the ranks of restored vehicles, while a few have slipped from Restored status to Restoration in Progress. This latter move is not always a retrograde step as sometimes a bus that has been previously restored and on static display for a number of years has been taken into the workshops to have attention to some major restoration job carried out, which will bring it back to operating condition in the not too distant future.

Some very familiar buses seen on rally sites up and down the country have been around for up to 30 years now so it is hardly surprising that they need more than a bit of tender loving care from time to time. Many of the vehicles listed have now been in preservation for far longer than they were in service and their continued well-being is due to the many thousands of hours that their owners have lavished on them over the years. This treatment is likely to be in marked contrast to the battering they frequently received in service from some passengers and crews. Starting restoration on a recently withdrawn bus can be a daunting task as you realise just how many things need attention.

So why would you want to preserve a bus? To those of us daft enough to take up the idea, it seems like quite a normal thing to do — after all, haven't all our friends got an old bus as well? To the general public, including family and colleagues, buying an old worn-out bus is only one step away from madness (and which of us would not agree when crawling under a filthy bus on a cold, damp January afternoon?). However, we don't usually preserve a bus or coach to enhance our 'street cred' or to look cool, for if those were our aims I doubt we would be in the hobby at all.

The reasons for buying a particular vehicle are many and varied and are often related to childhood memories and to the vehicles we remember travelling on at the age of about 10 or 12. Coaches can hold particularly special memories of family holidays to the coast and school trips with your friends. Others buy buses and coaches because they particularly admire the quality of workmanship and engineering skills that went into creating a robust, reliable machine — in much the same way as a car enthusiast might buy a classic Jaguar or Rover. Yet more buyers may have driven the vehicles in service and, having come to terms with the heavy controls and sometimes reluctant gear changes, derive a certain pleasure from driving them properly, as they were meant to be driven.

The above explains why individuals might decide to buy a bus or coach, but a museum has a different set of objectives to meet. It will have a Collecting Policy to define what sort of vehicles it should collect, probably from what geographical area they should originate, what technical advances they should display or even features peculiar to their local area. While most collections can therefore establish which buses and coaches they ought to add to the collection, the vehicles that actually form part of that collection may well be rather different. This is especially true of those museums whose collections are partly made up of privately owned vehicles although most have balanced their collections with their own acquisitions and any additional private applications to add vehicles to a collection will be tested against the criteria laid down in the Collecting Policy.

As vehicle preservation only really started in the late 1950s, only a small proportion of the historic buses in existence today date from before the end of World War 2. Early buses from the 1920s and before were developing rapidly and had relatively short lives. Their timber-framed bodies did not last long as the solid tyres jolted along the cobbled streets and quickly rotted away in Britain's damp climate. Even the technically advanced buses and coaches of the 1930s saw years of hard work during the war and only a few survived to be preserved, with a number of examples tantalisingly being scrapped just as the preservation movement was gaining momentum.

However, there are many more buses and coaches from the postwar era and it could be said that many collections have too high a proportion of such vehicles. That then poses the question 'Are there too many postwar, or too few prewar buses and coaches?' We certainly need to safeguard the future of those prewar vehicles we do have and also to continue to recover and conserve the remains of those unrestored examples which still turn up from time to time in barns, orchards, scrap-yards and even as summer houses. We need look no further than the fine collection of historic buses rebuilt by Mike Sutcliffe to see just what can be achieved from what might look like a very unpromising kit of rotted parts. With significant investment of time and money into those surviving prewar vehicles, we can redress the balance and provide a fuller picture of the development of road passenger transport in Britain.

What of the more recent vehicles? Are there too many in existence? If there are too many, which ones should be assured of a long-term future and which ones (if any) can we allow to fade away or even to be scrapped? How do we determine what is a valuable vehicle and which is of less significance?

In order to address these questions and also the resources needed to assure their future, NARTM has been working with the Transport Trust to carry out a survey of those buses and coaches in preservation, with special reference to their condition and accommodation. The database forming the basis for this present book is part of that survey and it will eventually help in showing which vehicle types are under- and over-represented and give an indication of the importance of retaining any particular vehicle which may be under threat in the future. Not all buses in existence are included in the current edition and it will be some time before the database can be considered to be a definitive list.

NARTM is also in the process of establishing significant stages in the development of the motorbus and coach, examples of which should be saved for future generations. That is not to say that all other vehicles should be disposed of — far from it, for there are many of local importance which are not technically special but which are of great value as part of the social history of an area. In addition, because many buses are owned privately, no one can presume to tell their owners what vehicles they should or should not own. In the historic bus world these are emotive subjects and there will be as many champions for particular buses and types of bus as there are vehicles.

At some point, however, an objective view will need to be taken to establish which vehicles are worthy of an assured future, possibly even a future supported by pubic funding. Unfortunately it is unlikely that all those buses and coaches in existence today will survive in the long term, although who would have predicted 35 years ago just how many steam railway engines would still be in working order in the 21st century? It is hoped that NARTM and its member organisations can play their part in raising the profile of historic buses and coaches and also work towards providing that long-term future for as many vehicles as reasonably possible. In the mean time, we hope that you enjoy browsing through this book and that you will be encouraged to visit many of the collections described in its pages.

Visiting Netley in 2000 was Southern Vectis 563, a 1959 Bristol LD6G. *Philip Lamb*

What is NARTM ?

The National Association of Road Transport Museums (NARTM) is an informal organisation of museums and collections. Volunteers operate many of them, although others, such as the Glasgow and London Transport Museums, are managed by full-time staff. This mix of museum types gives the opportunity to share ideas and experiences and the volunteers involved each bring their own professional skills to their projects and best practices can then be shared by all the member collections.

NARTM has been in existence for almost 20 years and now has around 30 member organisations, with more joining each year. The buses and coaches that form part of the NARTM collections are generally regarded as forming the nucleus of the National Collection of Buses and Coaches. However, it must be stressed that many important examples are in private hands outside the scope of NARTM and its members.

What does NARTM do?

Many of the people involved in running transport museums are busy people and have little spare time after making significant contributions to their own projects, such as this Museum in Manchester. This is why NARTM only holds two meetings each year at the various member museums and in recent years we have visited Devon, Lincoln, Glasgow, Oxford and Portsmouth. In between meetings, the quarterly *Bulletin* keeps members in touch with each other and we are often in touch. Indeed, one of the main functions of NARTM is to put people in touch with each other and there are many instances of restoration projects progressing and spare parts being located through NARTM contacts. Discussion topics at recent meetings have included the encouragement and role of Junior members, bus services, grant applications, museum registration, visitor facilities, risk assessment, documentation and links with other bodies.

NARTM's unique service to its members is also as an information exchange about running museums — after all, as so many of our members are volunteers, their skills and experiences are not within the heritage and leisure industry. It is often the case that another project in another area has already been faced with exactly the same issues as we have today, and by sharing ideas and pooling resources, progress can be made more quickly.

Over the years NARTM has also taken a lead role in campaigning on new legislation to lessen its impact on the historic bus preservation movement. Vehicle licensing, driver licensing, tachographs and the retention of original registration numbers have all received our attention, with some success in each case through our work in conjunction with other groups within the movement. NARTM is also a club authorised to endorse applications from historic vehicle owners to retain, or regain, the original registration of their vehicle.

The future

NARTM is currently working closely with the Transport Trust to define the bus preservation sector of the heritage transport industry. It is also addressing the major issues currently facing the movement — storage, documentation, human resources and skills, public access and the future of vehicles in preservation. A database is now maintained which lists all vehicles in NARTM and associated collections and this will eventually form part of a decision-making process to ensure that the most historically important vehicles have a secure long-term future.

For more information about NARTM please contact NARTM, PO Box 5141, Burton-upon-Trent, Staffordshire, DE15 0ZF.
Website: www.nartm.org.uk
e-mail: nartm@btinternet.com

Useful addresses

The Transport Trust, 202 Lambeth Road, London SE1 7JW.

British Bus Preservation Group, 18 Greenriggs, Hedley Park, Stopsley, Luton LU2 9TQ.

The PSV Circle, 26 Ashville Grove, Halifax HX2 0PN.

Preserving and Restoring a Bus

How does one go about restoring a bus to its former glory? No two vehicles will have to go through exactly the same stages, but the process and areas needing attention are usually very similar.

The starting point is generally a vehicle in run-down condition — which is why it was taken out of use in the first place. If it could have been economically repaired in the commercial environment, its owner would have done just that. Other buses may be in an even worse state, having lingered in a scrapyard or even as a hen-house or storeshed for a number of years. Some may be no more than bare, rusty chassis, their bodywork having succumbed to the elements!

Restoration work can be roughly divided into three main areas: chassis and mechanical parts, body structure and interior. The last is the most familiar to the public and the enthusiast, as it is the area most visible day-to-day. However, with its upholstery and detailed trim, it can be the hardest area to restore so that it looks and feels right.

Hopefully, the body structure will be in better shape. This will depend on whether the bus has been kept undercover, and on whether it has a timber or a metal frame. Each type of frame has its own problems, but these are made worse by the

Below: Two vehicles awaiting restoration at the Birmingham & Midland Museum of Transport are one-time Sheffield 271 (OWE 271K), a 1972 Bristol VR/East Lancs, and former Midland Red 6015 (GHA 415D), a 'D12' class Daimler Fleetline/Alexander of 1966. Limited restoration work appears to have started on the latter, as the paintwork has been rubbed down and some panels have been replaced. *Stephen Morris*

Right: Former London Transport 1937 AEC Regent STL2377 undergoes restoration at Cobham Bus Museum. *Philip Lamb*

damp climate which will usually have penetrated to start the processes of rotting and corrosion. When working on this part of the bus it is important to ensure that the bus remains 'square' and is not allowed to go out of shape by the removal of too many parts at the same time.

The mechanical parts will often be the least familiar to the enthusiast, but they are really the most important as they are the major organs of the vehicle. The chassis itself is fairly unlikely to have suffered more than surface rust, and much of the work underneath the bus will consist of scraping off accumulated mud, oil and grease. The major areas needing attention are likely to be the brakes, oil seals and the exhaust system. The engine may well be in running order but, if it makes loud knocking-sounds or produces a lot of smoke, further work will be needed. The wiring system is another part of the vehicle which will often require replacement, especially if old types of cable were used — these will probably have perished, leaving the vehicle in a dangerous condition where short circuits (leading to fire) are likely.

It is important that each stage of the restoration be documented, ideally in a formal way. This will ensure that future generations know what has been done to the vehicle — where materials have been replaced with newer ones, and where additions such as direction indicators have been made for safety reasons. These latter details are what differentiate restoration from conservation, although both approaches produce fine-looking vehicles in near-original condition.

When the basic condition of the vehicle is satisfactory, coach-painting of the exterior can be attempted; this can be one of the most satisfying stages of bus restoration, or one of the most exasperating! When all is complete, the owner should report to the local Vehicle Inspectorate depot and, with any luck, come away with a Test Certificate.

Below: The final touches are applied to former Widnes Leyland National No 1 (RTC 645L) at St Helens Transport Museum. *Philip Lamb*

Right: The finished article! Restored to its former glory is former Walsall 116 (XDH 516G), one of the municipality's final, 1969 batch of short Daimler Fleetlines with Northern Counties bodywork. *Stephen Morris*

How to Use this Book

This book lists both formal museums and the more informal types of collection, and gives details of opening times, contact addresses and the facilities available, together with a list of the buses, trolleybuses and coaches on display. Many of the sites are open to the public on a regular basis. Admission fees vary and some are even free to visitors, although donations towards the upkeep of the collections are always welcome. Please be aware that the vehicles on display can vary from time to time. Not all museums are able to display their entire 'fleet', and some practice the regular rotation of exhibits for added interest. In addition, some of the vehicles may be in the process of restoration in a workshop off-site, and there is always the possibility that a bus may be on loan to another museum! Visitors wishing to see a particular vehicle should make enquiries prior to the visit.

Some collections are not normally available for public access. However, the owners usually welcome visitors and will arrange for viewing by prior application. In addition, many such groups do have open or public days from time to time. Contact addresses are provided in this book, and those wishing to visit a particular site are asked to contact the address given. Please bear in mind that most are run by volunteers — please enclose a stamped self-addressed envelope when writing and respect the privacy of individuals. This book does not grant or imply any permission whatsoever to enter premises to look at old buses except by the agreement of the group involved. Note that, where buses are licensed for use on public passenger-carrying services, the use of individual vehicles will vary from time to time, as the demands of their preservation dictate.

Whilst some of the restored vehicles detailed here have been 'officially' preserved by their former operators, the majority have been restored and conserved by volunteers, often working in difficult conditions with limited resources of time, money and materials. That there are so many buses and coaches fully restored is a testimony to the dedication of bus enthusiasts over the last 40 years or more, and it is intended that the vehicles will have a long and secure future.

The information used in this book is as provided by the organisations listed, for which the authors express their thanks. As far as possible, details are correct to 30 September 2000. Any information on further collections not included in the current edition will be most welcome. If you own vehicles, or are associated wih such an organisation, please contact NARTM at the address given on page 9.

Left: Acquired by the SELNEC Preservation Society in 2000, former Greater Manchester 1451, the prototype Northern Counties-bodied Leyland Olympian latterly saw service with MK Metro as its 268. *Philip Lamb*

Right: Restored last year, the Telford Bus Group's Plaxton Elite II-bodied Bedford VAL70, WWY 115G was new to Abbey Coachways of Selby. *Philip Lamb*

For each vehicle, details given include the present registration number, year first registered, brief chassis and body details (including seating) and original operator. Standard PSV Circle body codes are used, as outlined below.

Body type (before seating capacity):
A	articulated
B	single-deck bus
C	coach (single-deck)
CH	double-decker coach
Ch	charabanc
CO	convertible open-top double-decker
DP	dual-purpose (eg coach seats in bus shell)
F	full-front (where not normal for chassis)
H	Highbridge double-decker
L	Lowbridge double-decker (ie with sunken side gangway upstairs; all other types — with conventional gangways — are 'H', regardless of overall height)
O	open-top double-decker
OB	open-top single-decker
PO	partially-open-top double decker
R	single-decker with raised rear saloon (eg over luggage compartment)
T	Toastrack

Seating capacity:
For double-deckers this is shown with the upper-deck capacity first , eg 43/31

Door position (after seating capacity):
C	centre entrance/exit
D	dual doors (usually front entrance and centre exit)
F	front or forward entrance/exit
R	open rear platform
RD	rear entrance/exit with doors
RO	open rear platform with open staircase
T	triple doors (eg on articulated vehicles)

Suffix:
t	fitted with toilet
l	fitted with wheelchair lift

The restoration state is given in accordance with the following code:
R	restored;
RP	restoration in progress;
A	awaiting restoration.

Seen visiting the Black Country Museum is 1953
Guy Arab IV/Metro-Cammell, Birmingham 2976,
normally to be seen at the Birmingham &
Midland Museum of Transport at Wythall.
Philip Lamb

Part 1
Museums Normally Open to the Public

Key to facilities			
A	Audio/visual displays	H	Baby-changing facilities
B	Bus rides (regular)	L	Lecture theatre
B(e)	Bus rides (at events)	M	Band stand
C	Children's information pack	P	Car parking
D	Access for disabled	R	Refreshments
E	Picnic facilities	S	Enthusiasts' shop
F	School activity pack	T	Toilets
G	Gift shop		

Abbey Pumping Station Leicester

Contact address: Corporation Road, Leicester LE4 5PX
Phone: 0116 299 5111
Fax: 0116 299 5125
Brief description: The Museum is a Victorian pumping-station dating from 1892 with four beam-engines. The vehicle collection is on view on special open days. On these occasions, one of the beam-engines is steamed.
Events planned: Please see the enthusiast press for details.

Opening days/times: Mon-Sat: 10.00 to 16.00 (17.00 in summer)
Sun: 14.00 to 16.30 (17.00 in summer)
Directions by car: A6 (north of Leicester) joins Abbey Lane at Redhill Island. Corporation Road is off Abbey Lane.
Directions by public transport: From City Centre (Charles Street) take bus 54 to top of Corporation Road.
Charges: Free except on special open days.
Facilities: C D E G H P R (on open days) T

Registration	Date	Chassis	Body	New to	Fleet No	Status
CBC 921	1939	AEC Renown 0664	Northern Counties H32/32R	Leicester City Transport	329	R
GAY 171	1950	Leyland Tiger PS1/1	Willowbrook DP35F	Allen, Mountsorrel	43	A
MTL 750	1958	Leyland Tiger Cub PSUC1/2	Yeates DP43F	Delaine Coaches, Bourne	47	R
TBC 164	1958	Leyland Titan PD3/1	Willowbrook H41/33R	Leicester City Transport	164	R
JMC 121K	1972	AEC Reliance 6MU4R	Plaxton C34C	Glenton Tours, London	121	R
OUM 727P	1976	Bedford J2SZ10	Caetano C16F	Anderton Tours, Keighley		R
B401 NJF	1984	Ford Transit 190D	Rootes B16F	Midland Fox	M1	R

Notes:
CBC 921   On view at Snibston Discovery Park

Amberley Museum

Contact address: Amberley, Arundel, West Sussex, BN18 9LT
Phone: 01798 831370
Fax: 01798 831831
E-mail: office@amberleymuseum.co.uk
Brief Description: The industrial museum has a wide range of attractions, including rail and bus operations. Some buses in the collection are museum-owned and others are owned by the Southdown Omnibus Trust or are in private hands.
Events planned: 16 September 2001 — AEC Bus & Coach Rally.
Opening days/times: March to October: Weds to Sun (also Mon

and Tues during school holidays)
Directions by car: Situated close to Amberley railway station on the B2139. Approach from the north and west via the A29 and from the east via the A24 and A283.
Directions by public transport: Hourly rail service calls at Amberley station which is adjacent to the museum.
Charges: Adults £6.50, Child £3.50, Family £18.00, Over 60s/Students £5.80.
Facilities: A B B(e) C D E F G H L P R T

Registration	Date	Chassis	Body	New to	Fleet No	Status
IB 552	1914	Tilling Stevens TS3 Petrol Electric	Newman O22/16R	Worthing Motor Services		R
CD 5125	1920	Leyland N	Short O27/24R	Southdown Motor Services	125	R
CD 4867	1923	Tilling Stevens TS3A Petrol Electric	(chassis only)			RP
BP 9822	1924	Shelvoke & Drewery Freighter	Hickman (Replica) B18C	Tramocar, Worthing		R
UF 1517	1927	Dennis 30cwt	Short B19R	Southdown Motor Services	517	R
MO 9324	1927	Tilling Stevens B9A	Brush B32R	Thames Valley Traction Co	152	R
BR 7132	1929	Leyland Lion LT1	Leyland B34F	Sunderland Corporation	2	R
UF 6473	1930	Leyland Titan TD1	Leyland H24/24R	Southdown Motor Services	873	R
UF 6805	1930	Tilling Stevens B10 A2	Short B31R	Southdown Motor Services	1205	RP
UF 7428	1931	Leyland Titan TD1	Short H26/24R	Southdown Motor Services	928	R
EUF 184	1938	Leyland Titan TD5	Leyland	Southdown Motor Services	0184	A

Notes:

IB 552	Petrol-Electric Transmission. Body new 1909.	
CD 5125	Restored using a P or Q, 5 or 6 ton chassis. Rebodied 1928	
CD 4867	Petrol-electric.To be restored as Southdown replica	
BP 9822	Solid tyres. Replica body built at Amberley	

UF 1517	All-metal body.	
MO 9324	Mechanical Transmission. Restored at Amberley	
UF 6805	Mechanical Transmission.	
EUF 184	Converted from bus 184; fitted with breakdown vehicle body ex Leyland TD1 872 (UF 6472)	

Above: 1927 Brush-bodied Tilling-Stevens B9A, Thames Valley 152 was restored at Amberley in 1997.
Nigel Appleford

Right: One of the earliest buses in regular use is Amberley Museum's 1914 Newman-bodied Tilling-Stevens TS3 Petrol-Electric IB 552, new to Worthing Motor Services, later absorbed by Southdown.
Nigel Appleford

Aston Manor Road Transport Museum

Contact address: The Old Tram Depot, 208-216 Witton Lane, Aston, Birmingham B6 6QE
Phone: 0121 322 2298
Fax: 0121 308 0544
Affiliation: NARTM
Brief description: The 19th-century former tram depot houses a selection of buses, coaches, commercial vehicles and tramcar bodies in an authentic setting — the depot still has tram tracks and stone sets in situ. There are also many small exhibits, working model layouts and video presentations.

Events planned:
28 May 2001 — Two Museums Running Day. Bus service linking Aston Manor and Wythall.
8 July 2001 — Open day/vehicle gathering.
16 Sept 2001 — Outer Circle Rally at Cannon Hill Park.
25 Nov 2001 — Collectors' fair with free bus rides.
Please see the enthusiast press for other events.

Opening days/times:
Saturdays, Sundays and Bank Hols 11.00 to 17.00. Other times by arrangement.
Opening times may vary during September and over Christmas/New Year period.
Directions by car: Easy access from M6 junction 6.
Directions by public transport: Rail to Witton Station and a short walk (170yd).
Bus No 7 from Birmingham City Centre or bus No 11, outer circle to Witton Square.
Charges:
Adults £1, Child 50p, Family £2.75.
Admission charges may vary on special event days.
Facilities: A B(e) D P R S T
Other information: Not all of the vehicles listed are on display at the museum. To view any vehicle not normally accessible, visitors should enquire at the museum as to arrangements for viewing.

Registration	Date	Chassis	Body	New to	Fleet No	Status
note z	1925	AEC S	Buckingham	Birmingham Corporation Tramways	215	A
OP 237	1926	(body only)	Short H32/26R	Birmingham Corporation Tramways	208	A
EA 4181	1929	Dennis E	Dixon B32F	West Bromwich Corporation	32	RP
HA 4963	1930	SOS RR	Brush	BMMO ('Midland Red')	963	A
JF 2378	1931	AEC Regal 662	Burlingham C32R	Provincial, Leicester	R1	R
note x	1931	SOS IM4	(chassis only)	BMMO ('Midland Red')		RP
OJ 9347	1933	Morris Commercial Dictator	Metro Cammell B—F	Birmingham Corporation Tramways	47	A
ANB 851	1934	Crossley Mancunian	Crossley/MCT H28/26R	Manchester Corporation	436	RP
AOG 679	1935	Daimler COG5	-	Birmingham Corporation Tramways	83	RP
CDH 501	1935	Dennis Lance	Park Royal H28/24R	Walsall Corporation	110	A
EHA 775	1938	SOS SON	English Electric	BMMO ('Midland Red')	2207	A
FON 630	1942	Leyland Titan TD7	(chassis only)	Birmingham City Transport	1330	A
DDM 652	1946	Maudslay Marathon II	Duple C33F	Rhyl United Coachways		R
KTT 689	1948	Guy Vixen	Wadham FC29F	Court Cars, Tourquay		R
JHA 890	1949	BMMO S8	Metro Cammell B40F	BMMO ('Midland Red')	3290	A
KHA 352	1950	BMMO CL2	Plaxton C26C	BMMO ('Midland Red')	3352	RP
JOJ 526	1950	Guy Arab IV	Metro Cammell H30/24R	Birmingham City Transport	2526	A
JOJ 548	1950	Guy Arab IV	Metro Cammell H30/24R	Birmingham City Transport	2548	RP
SB 8155	1950	Guy Wolf	Ormac B20F	Alexander MacConnacher, Ballachulish		R
JOJ 257	1950	Leyland Tiger PS2	Weymann B34F	Birmingham City Transport	2257	A
JOJ 222	1950	Leyland Titan PD2/1	Park Royal H29/25R	Birmingham City Transport	2222	RP
KEL 131	1950	Leyland Titan PD2/3	Weymann FH33/25D	Bournemouth Corporation	131	RP
GUJ 608	1950	Sentinel STC4	Sentinel B40F	Sentinal demonstrator		R
MLL 584	1951	AEC Regal IV 9821LT RF	Metro Cammell B37F	London Transport	RF 197	R
JOJ 707	1951	Daimler CVD6	Metro Cammell H30/24R	Birmingham City Transport	2707	R
RSK 615	1951	Leyland Royal Tiger PSU1/15	Duple DP41F	Jackson, Castle Bromwich		R
LLU 613	1952	AEC Regent III O961 RT	Weymann H30/26R	London Transport	RT 3254	RP
JOJ 847	1952	Daimler CVG6	Crossley H30/25RD	Birmingham City Transport	2847	A
LOG 301	1952	Guy Arab IV	Saunders Roe H30/25R	Birmingham City Transport	3001	RP
LOG 302	1954	Daimler CLG5	Metro Cammell H30/25R	Birmingham City Transport	3002	R
MOF 90	1954	Guy Arab IV	Metro Cammell H30/25R	Birmingham City Transport	3090	RP
RRU 903	1955	Leyland Tiger Cub PSUC1/1	Park Royal B40F	Bournemouth Corporation	266	RP
773 FHA	1958	BMMO D9	BMMO H40/32RD	BMMO ('Midland Red')	4773	A
1294 RE	1959	Guy Arab LUF	Burlingham C41F	Harper Bros, Heath Hayes	60	A
WLT 506	1960	AEC Routemaster R2RH	Park Royal H36/28R	London Transport	RM 506	RP
966 RVO	1963	Bedford VAL 14	Yeates C50D	Barton Transport, Chilwell	966	R
3035 HA	1963	BMMO D9	BMMO O40/32RD	BMMO ('Midland Red')	5035	RP
6314 HA	1963	BMMO D9	BMMO H40/32RD	BMMO ('Midland Red')	5314	A

Registration	Date	Chassis	Body	New to	Fleet No	Status
334 CRW	1963	Daimler CVG6	Metro Cammell H34/29R	Coventry City Transport	334	RP
264 ERY	1963	Leyland Titan PD3A/1	Park Royal O41/33R	Leicester City Transport	264	R
6370 HA	1964	BMMO D9	BMMO H40/32RD	BMMO ('Midland Red')	5370	R
436 KOV	1964	Daimler Fleetline CRG6LX	Park Royal H43/33F	Birmingham City Transport	3436	A
EHA 415D	1966	BMMO D9	BMMO/Willowbrook H40/32RD	BMMO ('Midland Red')	5415	R
KOX 663F	1967	AEC Swift MP2R	MCW B37D	Birmingham City Transport	3663	RP
LHA 870F	1967	BMMO S21	BMMO DP49F	BMMO ('Midland Red')	5870	R
UHA 969H	1970	BMMO S23	BMMO/Plaxton B51F	BMMO ('Midland Red')	5969	A
XON 41J	1971	Daimler Fleetline CRG6LX	Park Royal H43/33F	West Midlands PTE	4041	R
HFL 672L	1973	Leyland Atlantean AN68/2R	Northern Counties H47/34F	Whippet Coaches, Fenstanton		R
JOV 714P	1976	Bristol VRTSL2/6LX	MCW H43/33F	West Midlands PTE	4714	R
OOX 816R	1977	Leyland National	Leyland National DP45F	West Midlands PTE	6816	A
WDA 700T	1979	Leyland Fleetline FE30AGR	MCW H43/33F	West Midlands PTE	7000	R
F685 YOG	1988	MCW Metrorider MF150/113	MCW B23F	West Midlands PTE	685	RP

Notes:

note z	Registration not known	RSK 615	Originally registered LOE 300
note x	Registration not known	LOG 302	Chrome-plated chassis exhibited 1952 Commercial Motor Show
OJ 9347	Renumbered 77 in 1935		
ANB 851	Rebodied 1938	RRU 903	Converted for OMO and rear door removed in 1957
AOG 679	Originally bus 679 with Northern Counties H26/22R body; rebodied 1947 as a van	3035 HA	Originally H40/32RD; converted to open-top by Marshall ('Obsolete Fleet'), London (OM6)
KHA 352	Rebodied 1963	264 ERY	Originally H41/33R
KEL 131	Built with twin staircases and dual doors		

A recent arrival at Aston Manor Road Transport Museum is 1963 Leyland PD3A/1 Park Royal ex-Leicester 264, Guide Friday's premier vehicle. Converted to open-top for use in Stratford-upon-Avon and subsequently Oxford, the bus is on long-term loan to the Museum. *Philip Lamb*

Contact address: Chapel Lane, Wythall, Worcestershire, B47 6JX
Phone: 01564 826471
E-mail: enquiries@bammot.org.uk
Web site: www.bammot.org.uk
Brief description: The collection is based on buses built and/or operated locally, plus others of significant PSV history. In addition, there is a unique collection of battery-operated road vehicles and a miniature passenger-carrying steam railway on site.
Events planned: Please see the enthusiast press for details, generally Bank Holidays or last Sunday of summer and autumn months.
Opening days/times: Saturdays, Sundays and Bank Holidays 11.00 to 17.00, Easter Sunday to end of October.

Directions by car: Wythall is on the main A435 Birmingham-Evesham road. The museum is next to Wythall Church. From M42 use junction 3 and head towards Birmingham.
Directions by public transport: Museum services operate on event days.
First Midland Red serves Wythall from Birmingham; travel West Midlands from Solihull. Neither operates on Sundays.
Wythall rail station is 25min walk from museum.
Charges: £1.50 but higher charges apply on event days (generally £3).
Facilities: B(e) E P S T
Other information: Refreshments available on event days.

Registration	Date	Chassis	Body	New to	Fleet No	Status
O 9926	1913	Tilling Stevens TTA2	Thomas Tilling O18/16RO	BMMO ('Midland Red')	26	RP
HA 3501	1925	SOS Standard	Ransomes Simms & Jefferies B32F	BMMO ('Midland Red')	501	A
CN 2870	1927	SOS Q	Brush B37F	Northern General Transport	321	RP
CC 7745	1928	SOS QL	Brush B37F	Royal Blue, Llandudno		A
OV 4486	1931	AEC Regent 661	Metro Cammell H27/21R	Birmingham Corporation Tramways	486	A
OV 4090	1931	Morris Commercial Dictator	Metro Cammell B34F	Birmingham Corporation Tramways	90	A
OC 527	1933	Morris Commercial Imperial	Metro Cammell H50R	Birmingham Corporation Tramways	527	A
AHA 582	1935	SOS DON	Brush B36F	BMMO ('Midland Red')	1703	A
RC 4615	1937	AEC Regal O662	Willowbrook B34F	Trent Motor Traction Co	714	R
CVP 207	1937	Daimler COG5	Metro Cammell H30/24R	Birmingham City Transport	1107	R
GHA 337	1940	SOS SON	Brush B38F	BMMO ('Midland Red')	2418	RP
HHA 637	1946	BMMO S6	Metro Cammell B40F	BMMO ('Midland Red')	3036	A
FFY 402	1947	Leyland Titan PD2/3	Leyland O30/26R	Southport Corporation	85	RP
JXC 432	1948	AEC Regent III O961 RT	Weymann H30/26R	London Transport	RT 624	A
KAL 579	1948	Daimler CVD6	Massey H33/28RD	W Gash & Sons, Newark	DD2	R
GUE 247	1948	Leyland Tiger PS1	Northern Coach Builders B34F	Stratford-upon-Avon Blue Motors	41	A
JRR 404	1948	Leyland Titan PD1	Duple L29/26R	Barton Transport, Chilwell	473	RP
HOV 685	1948	Leyland Titan PD2/1	Brush H30/24R	Birmingham City Transport	1685	R
HDG 448	1949	Albion Venturer CX19	Metro Cammell H30/26R	Cheltenham District Traction Co	72	R
FDM 724	1949	Foden PVD6	Massey H30/26R	E H Phillips Motor Services, Holywell		A
HWO 334	1949	Guy Arab III	Duple L29/26R	Red & White Services	34	R
FJW 616+	1949	Sunbeam F4	Park Royal H28/26R	Wolverhampton Corporation	616	A
NHA 795	1950	BMMO D5B	Brush H30/26RD	BMMO ('Midland Red')	3795	A
NHA 744	1950	BMMO S12	Brush B44F	BMMO ('Midland Red')	3744	RP
KFM 775	1950	Bristol L5G	ECW B35R	Crosville Motor Services	KG126	R
ORB 277	1950	Daimler CVD6	Duple C35F	Tailby & George ('Blue Bus Services'), Willington		R
JOJ 533	1950	Guy Arab IV	Metro Cammell H30/24R	Birmingham City Transport	2533	R
JOJ 245	1950	Leyland Tiger PS2/1	Weymann B34F	Birmingham City Transport	2245	RP
JUE 349	1950	Leyland Tiger PS2/3	Northern Counties H35/28F	Stratford-upon-Avon Blue Motors	33	RP
MXX 23	1952	AEC Regal IV 9821LT RF	Metro Cammell B41F	London Transport	RF 381	R
JOJ 976	1953	Guy Arab IV	Metro Cammell H30/25R	Birmingham City Transport	2976	R
PDH 808	1953	Leyland Royal Tiger PSU1	Park Royal DP40F	Walsall Corporationl	808	R
RDH 505	1953	Leyland Titan PD2/12	Roe FH33/23RD	Walsall Corporationl	815	A
SHA 431	1953	Leyland Titan PD2/12	Leyland H30/26RD	BMMO ('Midland Red')	4031	RP
FRC 956	1954	Leyland Titan PD2/12	Leyland H32/26RD	Trent Motor Traction Co	1256	R
UHA 255	1955	BMMO S14	BMMO B44F	BMMO ('Midland Red')	4255	A
XHA 482	1956	BMMO D7	Metro Cammell H37/26RD	BMMO ('Midland Red')	4482	R
XHA 496	1956	BMMO D7	Metro Cammell	BMMO ('Midland Red')	4496	A
SUK 3	1957	Guy Arab IV	Metro Cammell H33/27R	Wolverhampton Corporation	3	A

Above: The Birmingham & Midland Museum of Transport at Wythall houses the largest collection of ex-Midland Red buses anywhere today. Here we see BMMO D9 5399 alongside underfloor-engined D10 4943, one of only two built. *Philip Lamb*

Below: BaMMOT's CM6T 5656 looks resplendent alongside visiting S23 5956 in NBC-style livery. *Philip Lamb*

Above: Channel islands buses enjoyed long service lives, and consequently many have survived in preservation. This is Guernsey Railway 62 (8231), a Reading-bodied Albion Victor, now at Wythall, and registered HFO 742. *Philip Lamb*

Left: This South Yorkshire PTE Alexander-bodied Leyland Atlantean No 1790 later saw service with Rossendale before passing into preservation at Wythall. *Philip Lamb*

Registration	Date	Chassis	Body	New to	Fleet No	Status
UTU 596J	1957	Guy Otter NLLODP	Mulliner B26F	Douglas Corporation	9	A
HFO 742	1958	Albion Victor FT39	Reading B35F	Guernsey Railway Co	62	R
VVP 911	1958	Bedford SB3	Duple C41F	Sandwell Motor Co, Birmingham		R
WDF 569	1959	Leyland Tiger Cub PSUC1	Willowbrook DP41F	Soudley Valley Coaches, Cinderford		R
943 KHA	1960	BMMO D10	BMMO H43/35F	BMMO ('Midland Red')	4943	R
871 KHA	1960	BMMO D9	BMMO H40/32RD	BMMO ('Midland Red')	4871	A
802 MHW	1961	Bristol Lodekka FSF6G	ECW H34/26F	Cheltenham District Traction Co	6037	R
3016 HA	1962	BMMO D9	BMMO/LPC O40/32RD	BMMO ('Midland Red')	5016	R
5073 HA	1962	BMMO S15	BMMO B40F	BMMO ('Midland Red')	5073	R
248 NEA	1963	Daimler CVG6/30	Metro Cammell H41/33R	West Bromwich Corporation	248	R
6545 HA	1964	BMMO S16	BMMO B52F	BMMO ('Midland Red')	5545	R
CUV 219C	1965	AEC Routemaster R2RH/1	Park Royal CH36/29R	London Transport	RCL 2219	R
BHA 656C	1965	BMMO CM6T	BMMO C44Ft	BMMO ('Midland Red')	5656	R
BHA 399C	1965	BMMO D9	BMMO H40/32RD	BMMO ('Midland Red')	5399	R
BON 474C	1965	Daimler Fleetline CRG6LX	Marshall B37F	Birmingham City Transport	3474	R
EHA 767D	1966	BMMO S17	BMMO/Plaxton B52F	BMMO ('Midland Red')	5767	R
GHA 415D	1966	Daimler Fleetline CRG6LX	Alexander H44/33F	BMMO ('Midland Red')	6015	RP
HBF 679D	1966	Leyland Titan PD2A/27	Metro Cammell H36/28RD	Harper Bros, Heath Hayes	27	RP
GRY 60D	1966	Leyland Titan PD3A/1	Park Royal H41/33R	Leicester City Transport	60	R
JHA 868E	1967	BMMO S21	BMMO DP49F	BMMO ('Midland Red')	5868	R
KHW 306E	1967	Bristol RELL6L	ECW B53F	Cheltenham District Traction Co	1000	R
NJW 719E	1967	Daimler Roadliner SRC6	Strachan B54D	Wolverhampton Corporation	719	R
XDH 56G	1968	Daimler Fleetline CRC6-36	Northern Counties H51/34D	Walsall Corporationl	56	RP
KOX 780F	1968	Daimler Fleetline CRG6LX	Park Royal H43/33F	Birmingham City Transport	3780	R
NEA 101F	1968	Daimler Fleetline CRG6LX	Metro Cammell H42/31F	West Bromwich Corporation	101	A
UHA 956H	1969	BMMO S23	BMMO/Plaxton B51F	BMMO ('Midland Red')	5956	R
OTA 632G	1969	Bristol RELH6G	ECW C45F	Southern National Omnibus Co (Royal Blue)	1460	R
XDH 516G	1969	Daimler Fleetline CRG6LX	Northern Counties H41/27D	Walsall Corporation	116	R
SHA 645G	1969	Leyland Leopard PSU4A/4R	Plaxton C36F	BMMO ('Midland Red')	6145	A
UHA 981H	1970	BMMO S23	BMMO/Plaxton B51F	BMMO ('Midland Red')	5981	R
WNG 864H	1970	Bristol RELL6G	ECW DP50F	Eastern Counties Omnibus Co	RLE 864	A
FRB 211H	1970	Bristol VRTSL2/6LX	ECW H39/31F	Midland General Omnibus Co	322	R
OWE 271K	1972	Bristol VRTSL2/6LX	East Lancashire Coachbuilders H43/30F	Sheffield Transport	271	RP
CBD 778K	1972	Bristol VRTSL3SL6LX	ECW H39/31F	United Counties Omnibus Co	778	R
TCH 274L	1973	Bristol RELH6G	ECW DP49F	Midland General Omnibus Co	274	R
PHA 370M	1974	Ford R1014	Midland Red/Plaxton DP23F	Midland Red Omnibus Co	370	A
GNU 569N	1974	Leyland National 11351/1R	Leyland National B49F	Trent Motor Traction Co	422	R
JMY 120N	1974	Leyland National 11351/1R/EXC	Leyland National C—Ft	National Travel		A
JOV 613P	1975	Daimler Fleetline CRG6LX	Park Royal H43/33F	West Midlands PTE	4613	R
99-64-HB	1976	Den Oudsten LOK	Den Oudsten B35D	VAD, Ermele (Netherlands)	5656	A
KON 311P	1976	Leyland Fleetline FE30 ALR	Metro Cammell H43/33F	West Midlands PTE	6311	R
NOE 544R	1976	Leyland National 11351A/1R	Leyland National B49F	Midland Red Omnibus Co	544	RP
OJD 903R	1977	Leyland National 10351A/1R	Leyland National B36D	London Transport	LS 103	R
BOK 1V	1979	MCW Metrobus DR102	Metro Cammell	West Midlands PTE	2001	A
KVF 247V	1980	Bristol VRTSL3/6LXB	ECW H43/31F	Eastern Counties Omnibus Co	VR 247	R
JKW 290W	1981	Leyland Atlantean AN68B/1R	Alexander H45/29D	South Yorkshire PTE	1790	R

+Trolleybus

Notes:

RC 4615	Rebodied 1950	3016 HA	Originally H40/32RD; converted to open-top by Marshall ('Obsolete Fleet'), London (OM5)
FFY 402	Originally H30/26R		
KAL 579	Rebodied 1958	5073 HA	Reseated from DP40F in 1969
JUE 349	Rebodied 1963	CBD 778K	Modified to resemble VRTSL3 by United Counties
XHA 496	Converted to Breakdown Vehicle 1972	PHA 370M	Shortened by Midland Red in 1979
UTU 596J	Originally registered WMN 485	99-64-HB	Netherlands registration
HFO 742	Originally registered 8231	KON 311P	Gardner engine fitted in 1981
943 KHA	Entered service 1961		

Contact address: Tipton Road, Dudley, West Midlands DY1 4SQ
Phone: 0121 557 9643
Brief description: Tramway operation daily. Trolleybus operation on Sundays and Bank Holidays.
Opening days/times: Summer: daily 10.00-17.00. Winter (Nov-Feb): Wednesdays to Sundays 10.00-16.00. Some evening openings
Directions by car: M5 (junction 2) signposted on Motorway. follow signs on A4123 to 'Black Country living Museum'.

Directions by public transport: Central Trains to Tipton station. Travel West Midlands 311-313 to outside Museum. Services 311-317 also serve Dudley and Walsall. West Midlands Metro to Wednesbury station
Facilities: A, B, B(e)C, D, E, F, G, H, L, P, R, T
Contact (Transport Group): Black Country Museum Transport Group, 28 Farm Close, Etchinghill, Rugeley, Staffs WS15 2XT.

Registration	Date	Chassis	Body	New to	Fleet No	Status
UK 9978+	1931	Guy BTX	Guy H-/-R	Wolverhampton Corporation	78	A
DUK 833+	1946	Sunbeam W	Roe H32/28R	Wolverhampton Corporation	433	R
FEA156	1949	Daimler CVG5	Metro Cammell B38R	West Bromwich Corporation	156	RP
GEA 174	1952	Daimler CVD6	Weymann H30/26R	West Bromwich Corporation	174	R
TDH 912+	1955	Sunbeam F4A	Willowbrook H36/34RD	Walsall Corporation	862	R
SCH 237+	1960	Sunbeam F4A	Roe H37/28R	Derby Corporation	237	R
XDH 519G	1969	Daimler CRG6LX	Northern Counties H41/27D	Walsall Corporation	119	RP
+trolleybus						

Note:
DUK 833   Rebodied in 1959

1955 Willowbrook-bodied Sunbeam F4A 862 is a regular performer on the circuit at the Black Country Living Museum in Dudley. *Philip Lamb*

Bristol Aero Collection — Kemble

Contact address: Mr W. Staniforth 37 Corbett Road, Hollywood, Birmingham B47 5LP (SAE please)
E-mail: william.staniforth@virgin.net
Affiliation: NARTM
Location: Hangar A1, Kemble Airfield, Nr Cirencester, Gloucs GL7 6BA

Brief description: A display of Bristol buses housed in an aircraft hangar alongside a Bristol aircraft and other products from the companies originally founded by Sir George White.
Events planned: Please see the enthusiast press for details.
Opening days/times: Sundays April-October, 10.00-16.00. Private parties by arrangement.

Registration	Date	Chassis	Body	New to	Fleet No	Status
HW 6634	1929	Bristol B	(chassis only)	Bristol Tramways & Carriage Co		A
JHT 802	1946	Bristol K6A	ECW H30/26R	Bristol Tramways & Carriage Co	C3386	RP
KHW 630	1948	Leyland Titan PD1	ECW H30/26R	Bristol Tramways & Carriage Co	C4019	A
MHU 49	1949	Bedford OB	Duple B30F	Bristol Tramways & Carriage Co	207	RP
JEL 257	1949	Bristol K5G	ECW L27/28R	Hants & Dorset Motor Services	1238	A
LHW 918	1949	Bristol L5G	ECW B35R	Bristol Tramways & Carriage Co	2410	A
LFM 753	1950	Bristol L6B	ECW DP31R	Crosville Motor Services	KW172	R
CNH 699	1952	Bristol KSW6B	ECW L27/28R	United Counties Omnibus Co	860	A
NFM 67	1952	Bristol KSW6B	ECW H32/28R	Crosville Motor Services	MW435	A
OHY 938	1952	Bristol KSW6B	ECW L27/28RD	Bristol Tramways & Carriage Co	L8089	A
RTT 996	1954	Bristol Lodekka LD6B	ECW H33/27RD	Southern National Omnibus Co	1876	A
UHY 359	1955	Bristol KSW6B	ECW H32/28R	Bristol Tramways & Carriage Co	C8319	A
YHT 958	1958	Bristol Lodekka LD6B	ECW O33/25RD	Bristol Omnibus Co	L8462	R
980 DAE	1959	Bristol MW5G	ECW B45F	Bristol Omnibus Co	2960	A
904 OFM	1960	Bristol SC4LK	ECW C33F	Crosville Motor Services	CSG655	RP
Q507 OHR	1961	Bristol MW6G	ECW	Bristol Omnibus Co	W151	RP
7682 LJ	1962	Bristol Lodekka FL6G	ECW H37/33RD	Hants & Dorset Motor Services	1482	A
507 OHU	1962	Bristol Lodekka FLF6G	ECW H38/32F	Bristol Omnibus Co	7062	RP
862 RAE	1962	Bristol SUS4A	ECW B30F	Bristol Omnibus Co	301	R
RDB 872	1964	Dennis Loline III	Alexander H39/32F	North Western Road Car Co	872	RP
BHU 92C	1965	Bristol MW6G	ECW DP43F	Bristol Omnibus Co	2428	R
CWN 629C	1965	Bristol MW6G	ECW B45F	United Welsh Services	134	A
FHT 15D	1966	Bristol Lodekka FLF6G	ECW	Bristol Omnibus Co	7240	RP
DFE 963D	1966	Bristol Lodekka FS5G	ECW H33/27RD	Lincolnshire Road Car Co	2537	R
RDV 423H	1968	Bristol RELH6G	ECW C45F	Western National Omnibus Co (Royal Blue)	1472	R
LRN 60J	1970	Bristol VRLLH6L	ECW CH42/18Ct	W C Standerwick	61	R
GYC 160K	1971	Bristol LH6L	ECW B45F	Hutchings & Cornelius Services, South Petherton		RP
PUO 331M	1974	Bristol LH6L	Plaxton C41F	Royal Blue	1331	RP
HAX 399N	1975	Bristol LHS6L	Duple C35F	R I Davies & Son, Tredegar		RP
KHU 326P	1976	Bristol LH6L	ECW B43F	Bristol Omnibus Co	376	RP
KOU 791P	1976	Bristol VRTSL3/6LXB	ECW H39/31F	Bristol Omnibus Co	5505	RP
TWS 910T	1979	Bristol VRTSL3/6LXB	ECW H43/27D	Bristol Omnibus Co	5129	R
AHW 200V	1980	Bristol VRTSL3/6LXB	ECW H43/27D	Bristol Omnibus Co	5149	RP

Notes:

YHT 958	Originally H33/25RD
Q507 OHR	Originally coach 2111, registered 404 LHT; converted to breakdown vehicle in 1974
507 OHU	On display at Aston Manor Road Transport Museum
FHT 15D	Ex playbus; to become exhibition vehicle

British Commercial Vehicle Museum   Leyland

Contact address: King Street, Leyland, Lancashire, PR5 1LE
Phone: 01772 451011
Fax: 01772 623404
Brief description: A unique line-up of historic commercial vehicles and buses spans a century of truck and bus building. More than 50 exhibits are on display in this national collection.
Events planned: Please see the enthusiast press for details.
Opening days/times:
April to end of September: Sundays, Tuesdays, Wednesdays and

Bank Holidays, 10.00 to 17.00
October: Sundays only, 10.00 to 17.00
Directions by car: Close to the M6 Junction 28.
Directions by public transport:
By train to Leyland station (on West Coast main line).
Buses from Preston and Chorley bus stations.
Charges: Adult £4, Child/OAP £2, Family £10.
Facilities: A B(e) D F G L P R S T

Registration	Date	Chassis	Body	New to	Fleet No	Status
UL 1771	1929	Bean 30cwt	Birch B14F	Turner, Wandsworth		R
IF-14-62	1948	AEC Regal III O963	CCFL B16D	Carris, Lisbon	104	R
KYY 653	1950	AEC Regent III O961 RT	Weymann H30/26R	London Transport	RT 1798	R
XTC 684	1955	Leyland LFDD	Metro Cammell H37/24RD	Leyland Demonstrator		R
OED 217	1956	Foden PVD6	East Lancashire Coachbuilders H30/28R	Warrington Corporation	112	R
301 LJ+ + Trolleybus	1962	Sunbeam MF2B	Weymann H37/28D	Bournemouth Corporation	301	R

Notes:
IF-14-62   Portugese registration; rebodied 1972

Castle Point Transport Museum   Canvey Island

Contact address: 105 Point Road, Canvey Island, Essex SS8 7TP
Phone: 01268 684272
E-mail: Glynis@topolino.demon.co.uk
Affiliation: NARTM
Brief description: This historic former Canvey & District bus depot, built in 1935, houses approximately 35 commercial vehicles spanning the years 1944 to 1968. Exhibits include buses, coaches, lorries, fire engines and military vehicles. They can be seen in varying stages from the totally restored to those in need of complete restoration. Completely run by volunteers, membership of the society is available at £6 per annum.

Events planned: Please see enthusiast press for details
Opening days/times: Open on Sundays, April to October.
Directions by car: A130 to Canvey Island; follow brown tourism signs on reaching the island.
Directions by public transport: By rail to South Benfleet, then by bus to Leigh Beck, Canvey Island.
Charges: Free admission. Donations welcome. A charge is made on the Transport Show day in October.
Facilities: B(e) P T
Other information: Hot drinks available.

Registration	Date	Chassis	Body	New to	Fleet No	Status
JVW 430	1944	Bristol K5G	ECW L27/28R	Eastern National Omnibus Co	3885	R
FOP 429	1944	Daimler CWA6	Duple O33/26R	Birmingham Corporation Tramways	1429	R
MPU 52	1947	Leyland Titan PD1A	ECW L27/26R	Eastern National Omnibus Co	3991	RP
CFV 851	1948	Bedford OB	Duple C29F	Seagull Coaches, Blackpool		R
KGU 413	1949	AEC Regent III O961 RT	Weymann H30/26R	London Transport	RT 1544	R
LYR 997	1949	AEC Regent III O961 RT	Weymann H30/26R	London Transport	RT 2827	R
LHY 937	1949	Bristol K6B	ECW H31/28R	Bristol Tramways & Carriage Co	C3448	RP
NEH 453	1949	Leyland Titan OPD2/1	Northern Counties L27/26RD	Potteries Motor Traction Co	L453	R
ONO 49	1950	Bristol L5G	ECW B35R	Eastern National Omnibus Co	4029	R
PTW 110	1950	Bristol L6B	ECW FC31F	Eastern National Omnibus Co	4107	RP
VRF 372	1951	Foden PVRF6	Harrington C41C	Bassett's Coaches, Tittensor		RP
WNO 478	1953	Bristol KSW5G	ECW O33/28R	Westcliff-on-Sea Motor Services		R

Line up at Castle Point Transport Museum from left to right: 1954 Eastern National LD5G 4208, 1949-built RT1544 and 1954-built RT4497 — both London Transport Weymann-bodied AEC Regent IIIs. *John G. Lidstone*

Registration	Date	Chassis	Body	New to	Fleet No	Status
OLD 717	1954	AEC Regent III 0961 RT	Weymann H30/26R	London Transport	RT 4497	R
XVX 19	1954	Bristol Lodekka LD5G	ECW H33/25R	Eastern National Omnibus Co	4208	R
JAP 698	1954	Harrington Contender	Harrington C41C	Audawn Coaches, Corringham		RP
381 BKM	1957	AEC Reliance MU3RV	Harrington C41F	Maidstone & District Motor Services	C381	RP
PHJ 954	1958	Leyland Titan PD3/6	Massey L35/32R	Southend Corporation	315	RP
UHJ 842	1959	Bedford C4Z2	Duple C29F	Rochford Hospital (staff bus)		A
236 LNO	1959	Bristol Lodekka LDL6LX	ECW H37/33R	Eastern National Omnibus Co	1541	A
217 MHK	1959	Bristol MW6G	ECW DP41F	Eastern National Omnibus Co	480	R
SGD 407	1960	Leyland Titan PD3/2	Alexander H41/31F	Glasgow Corporation	L405	RP
373 WPU	1961	Guy Arab IV	Massey L34/33R	Moore Bros, Kelvedon		R
28 TKR	1962	AEC Reliance 2MU3RV	Harrington C29F	Maidstone & District Motor Services	C28	R
138 CLT	1962	AEC Routemaster R2RH	Park Royal H36/28R	London Transport	RM 1138	RP
SDX 57	1963	AEC Regent V 2D2RA	H37/28R	Ipswich Corporation	57	RP
918 NRT	1963	AEC Regent V MD3RV	Massey	Lowestoft Corporation	8	RP
CUV 233C	1965	AEC Routemaster R2RH/1	Park Royal H36/29RD	London Transport	RCL 2233	R
NTW 942C	1965	Bristol Lodekka FLF6G	ECW H38/32F	Eastern National Omnibus Co	2849	R
AVX 975G	1968	Bristol Lodekka FLF6LX	ECW H38/32F	Eastern National Omnibus Co	2614	RP
CPU 979G	1968	Bristol VRTSL6LX	ECW H39/31F	Eastern National Omnibus Co	3000	R

Notes:

JVW 430	Renumbered 1274 in 1954
FOP 429	Originally H33/26R; later operated by Eastern National Omnibus Co and Southend Corporation (244)
MPU 52	Renumbered 1121 in 1954
LHY 937	Renumbered 1541 in 1964
ONO 49	Renumbered 309 in 1954 and 1107 in 1964
PTW 110	Renumbered 328 in 1954
WNO 478	Built as H33/28R; numbered 1423 in 1954, passed to

Eastern National Omnibus Co in 1955, renumbered 2380 in 1964 and converted to open-top in 1965/6

XVX 19	Renumbered 1431 in 1954 and 2400 in 1964
JAP 698	Former Harrington demonstrator
236 LNO	Renumbered 2510 in 1964
217 MHK	Renumbered 1402 in 1964
AVX 975G	Delivered as CH37/18F; fitted with bus seats and renumbered 2946 in 1969

Cavan & Leitrim Railway   Dromod

Contact address: Michael Kennedy, Cavan & Leitrim Railway, Narrow Gauge Station, Station Road, Dromod, Co Leitrim, Eire
Phone/fax: 003537838599
Brief description: Half mile 3ft gauge steam railway with a collection of railway vehicles (steam, diesel, carriages, wagons and railcars) together with a selection of vintage road vehicles.
Events planned: 6 May 2001 — Annual Vintage Rally
Opening days/times:
Daily April-September. Rest of year by request

Directions by car: to Dromod on N4 from Dublin. R202 from Dromod, 500yds.
Directions by public transport: Train to Dromod Irish Rail station from Dublin Connolly (Dublin-Sligo line). Narrow gauge station next to main line.
Charges: Adults IR£3.50, Child IR£2.00, Family IR£8.00. Includes train ride and museum.
Facilities: B(e) C D E G R (on request) S T

Registration	Date	Chassis	Body	New to	Fleet No	Status
ZJ 5904	1949	Leyland Tiger OPS3/1	CIE	CIE	P164	R
FCI 323	1950	Bristol LL5G	ECW B39R	Crosville Motor Services	KG156	RP
IY 7383	1951	GNR Gardner	Dundalk B33R	Great Northern Railway (Ireland)	G389	R
IY 8044	1951	GNR Gardner	Dundalk B33R	Great Northern Railway (Ireland)	G396	A
ZO 6960	1953	Leyland Titan OPD2/1	CIE H37/31R	CIE	R541	RP
ZY 1715	1955	AEC Regal IV	B..F	Great Northern Railway (Ireland)		R
ILI 98	1958	Bristol SC4LK	ECW B35F	Eastern National omnibus Co	455	RP
3945 UE	1960	Leyland Tiger Cub	Park Royal B45F	Stratford-upon-Avon Blue Motors	45	A
AZD 203	1962	Leyland Leopard L2	CIE B45F	CIE	E140	R
EZH 155	1965	Leyland Leopard PSU3/4R	CIE B45F	CIE	C155	A

Notes

ZJ 5904	Converted to recovery vehicle by CIE in 1970.	ZY1715	Converted to railway carriage 1971.
FCI 323	Worked in Ireland for Scully Omnibus of Co Laois.	ADZ203	Worked on hire to County Donegal Railways
ZO 6960	Sole survivor of a batch of 6 airport buses.		

City of Portsmouth Preserved Transport Depot

Contact address: 48-54 Broad Street, Portsmouth PO1 2JE
Phone: 02392 818223
Fax: 02392 256602
E-mail: friends@cpptd.freeserve.co.uk
Web site: www.cpptd.freeserve.co.uk
Affiliation: NARTM
Brief description: 21 veteran and vintage buses, trams and trolleybuses are on display, most of which spent their working lives in the south of England. Up to 10 are available for bus rides on open days.
Events planned: Open days on second and last Sunday of every month.

Opening days/times: Second and last Sunday of every month: 10.00 to 17.00.
Directions by car: From M275 follow directions for Isle of Wight car ferry. At Cambridge Road roundabout go straight ahead into High Street. At the end, bear right into Broad Street. Museum is in Broad Street on right-hand side on corner of Seager's Court.
Directions by public transport: Bus 16A from Portsmouth Harbour station. Free vintage bus service on open days.
Charges: Free.
Facilities: B B(e) C D F S T.
Other information: Car parking nearby (fee payable).

Right: Southdown 401, a convertible Northern Counties-bodied Leyland PD3/4, spent most of its working life at Worthing but ended its days at Portsmouth, where it is now preserved at the City of Portsmouth Preserved Transport Depot. *Philip Lamb*

Registration	Date	Chassis	Body	New to	Fleet No	Status
note a	1876	Horse bus		G Wheeler, Fawley		A
BK 2986	1919	Thornycroft J	Dodson O18/16R	Portsmouth Corporation	10	R
RV 3411	1933	Leyland Titan TD2	English Electric/ Portsmouth Corporation	Portsmouth Corporation	17	R
RV 4649+	1934	AEC 661T	English Electric H26/24R	Portsmouth Corporation	201	RP
RV 6368	1935	Leyland Titan TD4	English Electric O26/24R	Portsmouth Corporation	8	R
ECD 524	1937	Leyland Cub KPZ2	Park Royal B20F	Southdown Motor Services	24	RP
EHO 228	1942	Guy Arab I	Reading H30/26R	Gosport & Fareham Omnibus Co	55	R
CTP 200	1944	Bedford OWB	Duple (replica) UB32F	Portsmouth Corporation	170	R
DTP 823	1947	Leyland Titan PD1	Weymann H30/26R	Portsmouth Corporation	189	RP
AHC 442	1951	AEC Regent III 9613A	Bruce H30/26R	Eastbourne Corporation	42	R
EHV 65	1951	Bedford OB	Duple B29F	East Ham Borough Council	-	R
LRV 996	1956	Leyland Titan PD2/12	Metro Cammell O33/26R	Portsmouth Corporation	4	R
ORV 989	1958	Leyland Titan PD2/40	Metro Cammell H30/26R	Portsmouth Corporation	112	RP
BBK 236B	1964	Leyland Atlantean PDR1/1MkII	Metro Cammell H43/33F	Portsmouth Corporation	236	R
PRX 206B	1964	Leyland Titan PD3/4	Northern Counties FCO39/30F	Southdown Motor Services	401	R
TBK 190K	1971	Leyland Atlantean PDR2/1	Seddon Pennine B40D+19	Portsmouth Corporation	190	R
JWV 275W	1981	Bristol VRTSL3/680	ECW H43/31F	Southdown Motor Services	275	RP

+ Trolleybus

Notes:

note a	Note a: Not registered	CTP 200	Replica body; wartime livery
BK 2986	Body is c.1910 ex-LGOC B-type	EHV 65	Preserved in Hants & Sussex livery
RV 3411	Converted to Tower Wagon in 1955	LRV 996	Originally H33/26R
RV 6368	Originally H26/24R	PRX 206B	Originally registered 401 DCD
EHO 228	Rebodied 1955		

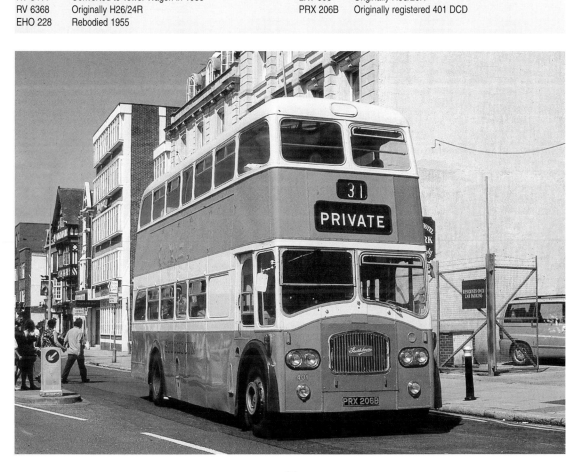

Cobham Bus Museum

Contact address: Redhill Road, Cobham, Surrey, KT11 1EF
Phone/Fax: 01932 868665
Affiliation: NARTM
Brief description: This well-established museum was formed by a small group of enthusiasts in 1966. The collection has steadily grown over the years and now over 30 preserved buses are located at Cobham.
Events planned: Please see the enthusiast press for details.
Opening days/times: Open days as advertised.

Viewing possible at weekends 11.00 to 17.00 but please telephone in advance to confirm.
Directions by car: From M25 junction 10 take A3 north and turn left on to A245. Museum is 1 mile on left.
Directions by public transport: Museum bus service from Weybridge station on main events.
Infrequent bus service at other times to Brooklands Road/Byfleet.
Charges: £2 but higher charges on open days.
Facilities: B B(e) G P R(limited) S T

Registration	Date	Chassis	Body	New to	Fleet No	Status
XX 9591	1925	Dennis 4-ton	Dodson O24/24RO	Dominion Omnibus Co		R
UU 6646	1929	AEC Regal 662	London General Omnibus Co B30R	London General Omnibus Co	T 31	R
GJ 2098	1930	AEC Regent 661	Thomas Tilling H27/25RO	Thomas Tilling		R
AXM 693	1934	AEC Regent 661	LPTB H30/26R	London Transport	STL 441	R
LJ 9501	1934	Albion Valiant PV70	Harrington C32F	Charlies Cars, Bournemouth	57	RP
CGJ 188	1935	AEC Q 0762	Birmingham R C & W B35C	London Transport	Q 83	R
CXX 171	1936	AEC Regal O662	Weymann C30F	London Transport	T 448	RP
DLU 92	1937	AEC Regent O661	LPTB H30/26R	London Transport	STL 2093	A
ELP 228	1938	AEC Regal O662	LPTB C30F	London Transport	T 504	R
EGO 426	1938	AEC Regent O661	LPTB H30/26R	London Transport	STL 2377	R
HGC 130	1945	Guy Arab II	Park Royal UH30/26R	London Transport	G 351	RP
HLX 410	1948	AEC Regent III O961 RT	Weymann H30/26R	London Transport	RT 593	R
UMP 227	1949	AEC Regal IV	Park Royal B40F	AEC prototype		A
MYA 590	1949	Leyland Comet CPO1	Harrington C29F	Scarlet Pimpernel, Minehead		R
JXC 288	1949	Leyland Tiger PS1	Mann Egerton B30F	London Transport	TD 95	R
KGK 803	1949	Leyland Titan 7RT	Park Royal H30/26R	London Transport	RTL 139	R
LUC 210	1951	AEC Regal IV 9821LT RF	Metro Cammell DP35F	London Transport	RF 10	RP
MLL 969	1952	AEC Regal IV 9821LT RF	Metro Cammell	London Transport	RF 332	R
NLE 534	1952	AEC Regal IV 9821LT RF	Metro Cammell B39F	London Transport	RF 534	R
LYR 826	1952	AEC Regent III O961 RT	Park Royal H30/26R	London Transport	RT 2775	RP
LYR 910	1952	AEC Regent III O961 RT	Park Royal H30/26R	London Transport	RT 3491	R
MLL 685	1952	Leyland Titan 7RT	Park Royal H30/26R	London Transport	RTL 1323	A
NLE 672	1953	AEC Regal IV 9821LT RF	Metro Cammell B41F	London Transport	RF 672	R
MLL 740	1953	AEC Regal IV 9822E	Park Royal HDC37C	British European Airways		R
MXX 334	1953	Guy Special NLLVP	ECW B26F	London Transport	GS 34	R
CDX 516	1954	AEC Regent III 9613E	Park Royal H30/26R	Ipswich Corporation	16	R
SLT 58	1958	Leyland Routemaster	Weymann H34/30R	London Transport	RML 3	R
EGN 369J	1971	AEC Swift 4MP2R	Park Royal B33D + 34	London Transport	SMS 369	R
JPA 190K	1972	AEC Reliance 6U2R	Park Royal DP45F	London Country Bus Services	RP 90	R
SPK 203M	1973	AEC Reliance 6U3ZR	Plaxton C49F	London Country Bus Services	P 3	R

Notes:

XX 9591	Restored as London General Omnibus Co D142	MYA 590	Converted from petrol to diesel in 1966
GJ 2098	On loan to BMMO during World War 2	JXC 288	Toured Europe and USSR 1963-1967
CXX 171	Used as an ambulance during World War 2	MLL 969	Converted to a towing vehicle in 1976
DLU 92	Original metal-framed Park Royal body replaced in 1949	LYR 910	Fitted with AEC 11.3 litre engine, 1998
ELP 228	Used as an ambulance during World War 2	LYR 826	Toured USA and Canada when new
HGC 130	Only remaining example of a London utility bus	SLT 58	Prototype Leyland Routemaster; renumbered RM3 in 1961
UMP 227	Prototype Regal IV - operated with London Transport in 1950		

Above: London Transport Q83, a BRC&W-bodied AEC Q was built in 1935. It has been at the Cobham Bus Museum for many years. *Philip Lamb*

Below: Built in 1949, this Harrington-bodied Leyland Comet CPO1 was new to Scarlet Pimpernel Coaches of Minehead, acquiring its present livery as a result of appearing in an episode of 'Miss Marple' television series. *Philip Lamb*

Left: One of a number of buses associated with the Dover Transport Museum is East Kent 6801 FN, a 1961 AEC Regent V, bodied by Park Royal. *Philip Lamb*

Below: Although the East Anglian Transport Museum is known for its trolleybuses, it is also home to a number of motorbuses, including London Transport RTL1050, a 1950 Leyland 7RT with Park Royal body. *Philip Lamb*

Dover Transport Museum
Whitfield

Contact address: Old Park, Whitfield, Dover, CT16 2HQ
Phone: 01304 822409/204612
Affiliation: NARTM, Transport Trust, AIM, ASTRO
Brief description: The museum displays local transport and social history. Road vehicles of all types. A maritime room, railway room, bygone shops and a garage. Hundreds of transport models including a working model tramway.
Events planned: Please see the enthusiast press for details.
Opening days/times: Easter to end June — Sundays 10.30 to 17.00;

July, August and September — Thursdays and Fridays 14.00 to 17.00; Sundays 10.30 to 17.00.
Open at other times for pre-arranged groups.
Directions by car: Approximately one mile from the A2 Whitfield roundabout on the Dover bypass.
Directions by public transport: Dover Priory station then bus to Old Park, Whitfield.
Charges: Adult £2, Senior Citizen £1.50, Child £1, Family £5.
Facilities: B(e) D E G P R T

Registration	Date	Chassis	Body	New to	Fleet No	Status
CC 9305	1929	Dennis G	Roberts T19	Llandudno UDC		R
WYJ 813	1934	Renault TN6C2	STRCP B33R	RATP (Paris)	2765	R
KHY 383	1948	Bristol L6B	Bristol Tramways & Carriage B35R	Bristol Tramways & Carriage Co	2382	R
KXW 488	1950	AEC Regent III O961 RT	Weymann H30/26R	London Transport	RT 1389	RP
KYY 872	1950	AEC Regent III O961 RT	Weymann H30/26R	London Transport	RT 3143	R
EFN 591	1950	Dennis Lancet J3	Park Royal C32F	East Kent Road Car Co		A
FNV 557	1950	Leyland Tiger PS2/3	Whitson FC33F	Church ('Royal Blue'), Pytchley		R
FFN 451	1951	Leyland Royal Tiger PSU1/13	Park Royal C37C	East Kent Road Car Co		RP
NKT 896	1951	Leyland Titan PD2/12	Leyland H30/28RD	Maidstone & District Motor Services	DH400	A
GFN 273	1952	Leyland Titan TD5	Beadle C35F	East Kent Road Car Co		R
PHJ 953	1958	Leyland Titan PD3/6	Massey O33/41R	Southend Corporation	314	R
569 KKK	1960	AEC Reliance 2MU3RA	Duple C41C	Ayers Coaches, Dover		R
6801 FN	1961	AEC Regent V 2D3RA	Park Royal H40/32F	East Kent Road Car Co		R
WFN 513	1961	AEC Reliance 2MU3RV	Park Royal DP41F	East Kent Road Car Co		R
AFN 780B	1963	AEC Regent V 2D3RA	Park Royal H40/30F	East Kent Road Car Co		R
GJG 751D	1966	AEC Regent V 2D3RA	Park Royal O40/32F	East Kent Road Car Co		R
JRJ 268E	1967	Leyland Titan PD2/40	MCW H36/28F	Salford Corporation	268	R
GFN 546N	1975	Leyland National 10351/1R	Leyland National B40F	East Kent Road Car Co	1546	RP

Notes:

KHY 383	Carries 1950 body	PHJ 953	Originally L35/33R; converted to open-top in 1971
EFN 591	Operated as a single-deck bus from June 1961	GJG 751D	Originally H40/32F; used as promotional vehicle
GFN 273	Rebuild of Leyland Titan TD5		

East Anglia Transport Museum
Carlton Colville

Contact address: Chapel Road, Carlton Colville, Lowestoft, Suffolk, NR33 8BL
Phone: 01502 518459
Affiliation: NARTM & London Trolleybus Preservation Society.
Brief description: A working transport museum on a four-acre site, first opened in 1972 and run entirely by volunteers. Tram and trolleybus services operate regularly within a developing street scene and the tramway has a woodland section. There is also a narrow-gauge railway. A wide variety of other vehicles on display and sometimes operated includes buses, lorries, steam rollers, battery-electrics, tower wagons and a London taxi. The museum is a registered charity.
Events planned:
24 June 2001 — Bygone Fire & Steam Event

8 July 2001 — Bus Event 2001
11/12 August 2001 — Classic Vehicle Weekend 2001
8/9 September 2001 — Trolleybus Weekend 2001
Opening days/times: At Easter, then from May to September:
Sundays and Bank Holidays — 11.00 to 17.30;
Wednesdays and Saturdays (June to Sept) — 14.00 to 17.00;
All other days (late July and Aug) — 14.00 to 17.00.
Directions by car: Situated on the A1384. Follow the brown signs from the A12, A146 and A1117.
Directions by public transport:
Monday to Saturday: Eastern Counties bus L11 or L12 from Lowestoft bus station to Carlton Colville Church, then 8min walk.
Sundays and Bank Holidays: Eastern Counties bus L18 or L19 from Lowestoft bus station to the Museum.

By train to Oulton Broad South then 35min walk.
Charges: £4.50 adults, £3 children/OAPs. Higher charges at special events. Admission includes free rides within the museum.

Facilities: B(e) D E F G H P R S T
Other information: Regular tram and trolleybus rides.

Registration	Date	Chassis	Body	New to	Fleet No	Status
AH 79505+	1926	Garrett O type	Strachan & Brown B26D	NESA Copenhagen	5	RP
KW 1961	1927	Leyland Lion PLSC3	Leyland B35F	Blythe & Berwick, Bradford		A
ALJ 986+	1935	Sunbeam MS2	Park Royal O40/29R	Bournemouth Corporation	202	R
CUL 260+	1936	AEC 664T	Metro Cammell H40/30R	London Transport	260	R
EXV 201+	1938	Leyland LPTB70	Leyland H40/30R	London Transport	1201	R
FXH 521+	1940	Metro Cammell	Metro Cammell H40/30R	London Transport	1521	R
GBJ 192	1947	AEC Regent II O661	ECW H30/26R	Lowestoft Corporation	21	R
note d+	1948	Berna	Hess B37D	Biel (Switzerland)	39	R
KAH 408	1948	Bristol L4G	ECW B35R	Eastern Counties Omnibus Co	LL 108	A
BDY 809+	1948	Sunbeam W	Weymann H30/26R	Hastings Tramways Co	34	RP
NBB 628+	1950	BUT 9641T	Metro Cammell H40/30R	Newcastle Corporation	628	A
LLU 829	1950	Leyland Titan 7RT	Park Royal H30/26R	London Transport	RTL 1050	R
ERV 938+	1951	BUT 9611T	Burlingham H28/26R	Portsmouth Corporation	313	A
SG 2030+	1952	Henschel UhIII/S	Uerdingen B32T	Solingen (Germany)	1	R
LCD 52+	1953	BUT 9611T	Weymann H30/26R	Brighton Corporation	52	R
DRC 224+	1953	Sunbeam F4	Willowbrook H32/28R	Derby Corporation	224	R
YTE 826+	1956	BUT 9612T	Bond H32/28R	Ashton under Lyne Corporation	87	R
2206 OI+	1958	Sunbeam F4A	Harkness H36/32R	Belfast Corporation	246	RP
YLJ 286+	1959	Sunbeam MF2B	Weymann H35/28D	Bournemouth Corporation	286	R
557 BNG	1962	Bristol Lodekka FL6G	ECW H37/33RD	Eastern Counties Omnibus Co	LFL 57	R
YRT 898H	1969	AEC Swift 2MP2R	ECW B45D	Lowestoft Corporation	4	R
OCK 985K	1972	Bristol VRTSL2/6LX	ECW H39/31F	Ribble Motor Services	1985	R
+ Trolleybus						

Notes:

AH 79505	Danish registration; being renovated in Copenhagen	LCD 52	Built 1950, first used 1953; preserved in colours of subsequent operator Maidstone Corporation
ALJ 986	Converted to open top 1958	2206 OI	Trolleybus fitted with hydraulic brakes
note d	Swiss Trolleybus; unregistered	OCK 985K	Acquired by Eastern Counties Omnibus Co (VR385) in 1985
SG 2030	German registration		

Imperial War Museum   London

Contact address: Lambeth Road, London SE1 6HZ
Phone: 0207 416 5320
0891 600140 (Recorded information)
E-mail: website: www.iwm.org.uk
Brief description: Revel in the history of the nation, through the world wars and much more besides. Regular exhibitions and displays of considerable educational value. The one bus in the collection fills a significant gap in transport history. Enquire before visiting on 020 7416 5211 to check bus is on display.
Opening days/times: Daily 10.00 to 18.00 (closed 24, 25 and 26 December)
Directions by car: South of Waterloo Station, close to the Elephant & Castle. Parking difficult but Coach Park at Vauxhall Bridge and disabled parking by prior arrangement only — phone 020 7416 5397.
Directions by public transport:
Underground to Lambeth North, Waterloo or Elephant & Castle. Rail to Waterloo.
Bus routes 1, 3, 12, 45, 53, 63, 68, 159, 168, 171, 172, 176, 188, 344 and C10.
Charges: Adult £5.20, Senior Citizen £4.20, Children free. Group rates available. Free after 16.30 daily.
Facilities: A C D G H R T

Registration	Date	Chassis	Body	New to	Fleet No	Status
LN 4743	1911	LGOC B	London General Omnibus Co O18/16RO	London General Omnibus Co	B43	R

Note:

LN 4743   Named *Ole Bill* after wartime cartoon character

Ipswich Transport Museum

Contact address: Old Trolleybus Depot, Cobham Road, Ipswich
IP3 9JD
Phone: 01473 715666
E-mail: www.ipswichtransportmuseum.co.uk.html
Affiliation: NARTM, ASTRO, TORA, SEMS, AFSM
Brief description: The collection includes most forms of road transport from the last 200 years, including bicycles, horse-drawn vehicles, trucks and service vehicles. There are displays of vehicles and other products of Ipswich engineering companies including six mobile cranes.
Events planned: 6 May 2001 — 31st Ipswich-Felixstowe Road Run
7 October 2001 — Annual 'Ride on our Buses' day

Opening days/times: April to November: Sundays and Bank Holidays 11.00 to 16.30
August and school half-term, Monday to Friday 13.00 to 16.00.
Directions by car: From A12/A14 junction with A1189 (Nacton and Ipswich East) head towards Ipswich on Nacton Road. Turn right into Lindburgh Road. Museum is on left in Cobham Road.
Directions by public transport: By train to Ipswich. Take any bus to Town Centre.
Then take bus 2 to Cobham Road (Mon-Fri) or bus 75/76/77 (Suns) to Felixstowe Road Railway bridge.
Charges: Adult £2.50, Child £1.50, Concessions £2, Family £7.
Facilities: A B(e) D G P R T, picnic area.

Registration	Date	Chassis	Body	New to	Fleet No	Status
DX 3988+	1923	Railless	Short B30D	Ipswich Corporation	2	R
DX 5629+	1926	Garrett O type	Strachan & Brown B31D	Ipswich Corporation	26	A
DX 5610+	1926	Ransomes Simms & Jefferies D	Ransomes Simms & Jefferies B31D	Ipswich Corporation	9	A
note c+	1926	Ransomes Simms & Jefferies D	(chassis only)	Ipswich Corporation	16	R
DX 6591	1927	Tilling Stevens B9B	Eastern Counties B36R	Eastern Counties Road Car Co	78	A
VF 2788	1928	ADC 425A	Eastern Counties B36R	United Automobile Services	J379	A
DX 7812	1929	Tilling Stevens B10 A2	(chassis only)	Eastern Counties Road Car Co	116	R
WV 1209	1932	Bedford WLB	Waveney B20F	Alexander, Devizes		A
PV 817+	1933	Ransomes Simms & Jefferies	Ransomes Simms & Jefferies H24/24R	Ipswich Corporation	46	A
CVF 874	1939	Bristol L5G	ECW B35R	Eastern Counties Omnibus Co	LL 574	A
CAH 923	1940	Dennis Ace	ECW B20F	Eastern Counties Omnibus Co	D 23	RP
PV 8270+	1948	Karrier W	Park Royal H30/26R	Ipswich Corporation	105	A
PV 9371	1949	Bedford OB	Duple C27F	Mulleys Motorways, Ixworth		R
KNG 374	1949	Bristol K6B	ECW L27/28R	Eastern Counties Omnibus Co	LK 374	A
KAH 407	1949	Bristol L4G	ECW B35R	Eastern Counties Omnibus Co	LL 407	RP
ADX 1	1950	AEC Regent III 9612E	Park Royal H30/26R	Ipswich Corporation	1	R
ADX 196+	1950	Sunbeam F4	Park Royal H30/26R	Ipswich Corporation	126	R
MAH 744	1951	Bristol LSX4G	ECW B42F	Eastern Counties Omnibus Co	LL 744	R
BPV 10	1953	AEC Regal IV 9822E	(chassis only)	Ipswich Corporation	10	A
BPV 9	1953	AEC Regal IV 9822E	Park Royal B42D	Ipswich Corporation	9	A
ADX 63B	1964	AEC Regent V 2D2RA	Massey H37/28R	Ipswich Corporation	63	R
APW 829B	1964	Bristol MW6G	ECW C39F	Eastern Counties Omnibus Co	LS 829	R
CNG 125C	1965	Bristol Lodekka FS5G	ECW H33/27RD	Eastern Counties Omnibus Co	LFS 125	RP
DPV 68D	1966	AEC Regent V 2D2RA	East Lancashire Neepsend H37/28R	Ipswich Corporation	68	A
JRT 82K	1971	AEC Swift 2MP2R	Willowbrook B40D	Ipswich Corporation	82	R
MRT 6P	1976	Leyland Atlantean AN68/1R	Roe H43/29D	Ipswich Corporation	6	R
XNG 770S	1978	Leyland National 11351/1R	Leyland National B—F	Eastern Counties Omnibus Co	LN 770	A

+ Trolleybus

Notes:

DX 3988	Believed the oldest trolleybus on display in the world	CVF 874	Originally numbered LL74
note c	Chassis only	CAH 923	Originally fitted with Gardner 4LK engine
DX 5610	Changed from solid to pneumatic tyres in 1930	PV 8270	Originally fitted with wooden seats
DX 6591	New with charabanc body; rebuilt in 1934	KNG 374	Engine changed Gardner 5LW by Eastern Counties OC
VF 2788	Original United body replaced in 1934	ADX 1	Ipswich Corporation's first motor bus
DX 7812	Rebodied twice while with Eastern Counties	MAH 744	Bristol LS prototype
PV 817	First Ipswich double decker		

Contact address: Seaclose Quay, Newport, Isle of Wight, PO30 2EF

Phone: 01983 533352

Affiliation: NARTM

Brief description: The collection ranges from a 1927 Daimler CK to a 1985 Ford Transit. Many of the vehicles are of Southern Vectis origin.

Events planned: 14 October 2001 — running day at Newport Quay. Please see enthusiast press for details.

Opening days/times: End May to end September: Sunday to Friday, 10.30 to 16.00

Directions by car: Access off Medina Way relief road and Sea Street. Left on to Quay. Bus museum is adjacent to Boat Museum (both signposted).

Directions by public transport: Bus to Newport bus station. Walk 12min to north of town.

Charges: £2 Adult, £1.50 Senior Citizen, £1 child.

Facilities: B(e) D G S

Other information: Car parking nearby. Refreshments and toilets at adjacent Boat Museum.

Registration	Date	Chassis	Body	New to	Fleet No	Status
DL 5084	1927	Daimler CK	Dodson B26R	Dodson Bros ('Vectis')	11	A
NG 1109	1931	Reo Pullman	Taylor Ch26D	Reynolds, Overstrand		
DL 9015	1934	Dennis Ace	Harrington B20F	Southern Vectis Omnibus Co	405	RP
AUF 666	1934	Leyland Titan TD3	Beadle H28/26R	Southdown Motor Services	966	RP
JT 8077	1937	Bedford WTB	Duple C25F	South Dorset Coaches		R
CAP 234	1940	Bristol K5G	ECW O58R	Brighton Hove & District Omnibus Co	903	RP
EDL 657	1947	Bristol K5G	ECW L27/28R	Southern Vectis Omnibus Co	721	RP
HDL 279	1951	Bristol LL5G	ECW B39R	Southern Vectis Omnibus Co	835	RP
ODL 399	1957	Bedford SBG	Duple C41F	Moss Motor Tours, Sandown		RP
ODL 400	1957	Bedford SBG	Duple C41F	Moss Motor Tours, Sandown		RP
PDL 519	1958	Bristol Lodekka LD6G	ECW CO33/27R	Southern Vectis Omnibus Co	559	A
PDL 515	1958	Bristol MW6G	ECW C39F	Southern Vectis Omnibus Co	315	RP
SDL 268	1959	Bristol Lodekka LD6G	ECW H33/27R	Southern Vectis Omnibus Co	563	R
TDL 998	1960	Bristol Lodekka FS6G	ECW H33/27R	Southern Vectis Omnibus Co	565	R
YDL 318	1962	Bristol Lodekka FS6G	ECW H33/27R	Southern Vectis Omnibus Co	573	R
CDL 479C	1965	Bristol Lodekka FLF6G	ECW H38/32F	Southern Vectis Omnibus Co	611	R
FDL 927D	1966	Bristol MW6G	ECW B43F	Southern Vectis Omnibus Co	806	R
KDL 885F	1968	Bristol RESH6G	Duple C45F	Southern Vectis Omnibus Co	301	R
VDL 264K	1972	Bedford YRQ	Plaxton B47F	Seaview Services		A
MDL 880R	1976	Leyland National	Leyland National B52F	Southern Vectis Omnibus Co	880	A
TDL 126S	1977	Bedford YRT	Duple C51F	Southern Vectis Omnibus Co	126	A
YDL 135T	1979	Ford R1014	Duple B47F	Isle of Wight County Council	5809	A
B259 MDL	1985	Ford Transit	Carlyle B16F	Southern Vectis Omnibus Co	259	A

Notes:

AUF 666	Rebodied 1949
CAP 234	Originally H56R Conv to open top 1952. Fleet No 6350 when new. To Southern Vectis 2/60.
PDL 519	Originally H33/27R
TDL 998	Owned by Southern Vectis and loaned to museum
YDL 318	Owned by Southern Vectis and loaned to museum
CDL 479C	Owned by Southern Vectis and loaned to museum
FDL 927D	Owned by Southern Vectis and loaned to museum
KDL 885F	Owned by Southern Vectis and loaned to museum

Keighley Bus Museum Denholme

Contact address: 47 Brantfell Drive, Burnley, Lancs BB12 8AW
Phone: 01282 413179 or 01274 587519
Affiliation: NARTM
Brief description: A collection of buses, coaches and ancillary vehicles. Some are owned by the Trust and others by private individuals. The Trust aims to establish a permanent home for the collection in central Keighley.
Events planned: 29 April, 12/3, 27 May, 3, 17 june, 1, 29 july, 26 August, 8, 30 September, 20/21 October, 25 December. most Sundays 12.00-16.00, Tuesday and Thursdays from 19.00.

Opening days/times: Currently under review, please enquire for details.
Directions by car: Between Keighley and Halifax, at Denholme. The Museum is located behind the Parish Church.
Directions by public transport: Frequent buses from Keighley to Denholme.
Charges: Special events: £2 Adult, £1 concession. Otherwise free but donations welcome.
Facilities: B(e) P T

Registration	Date	Chassis	Body	New to	Fleet No	Status
WT 7101+	1924	Straker Clough	Brush H50R	Keighley Corporation Tramways	5	R
KW 2260	1927	Leyland Lion PLSC3	Leyland B35R	Bradford Corporation	325	A
TF 6860	1931	Leyland Lion LT3	Leyland B36R	Rawtenstall Corporation	61	RP
ANW 682	1934	AEC Regent 661	Roe H30/26R	Leeds City Transport	139	R
DKT 11	1937	Leyland Tiger TS7	Harrington C32R	Maidstone & District Motor Services	CO553	A
CWX 671	1938	Bristol K5G	Roe L27/28R	Keighley-West Yorkshire Services	KDG 26	R
CFM 354	1938	Leyland Titan TD5	ECW L26/26R	Crosville Motor Services	M52	RP
EUF 198	1938	Leyland Titan TD5	Short	Southdown Motor Services	0198	R
RN 8622	1939	Leyland Titan TD5	Alexander L27/26R	Ribble Motor Services	2057	R
FWW 596	1947	Bedford OB	Duple C26F	West Yorkshire Road Car Co	646	A
CUH 856	1947	Leyland Tiger PS1	ECW B35R	Western Welsh Omnibus Co	856	A
HOD 30	1948	Bristol L6A	Beadle C31F	Western National Omnibus Co (Royal Blue)	1228	R
MNW 86	1948	Leyland Tiger PS1	Roe B36R	Leeds City Transport	28	R
FWX 914+	1948	Sunbeam F4	East Lancashire Coachbuilders H37/29F	Bradford Corporation	844	R
NNW 492	1949	AEC Regent III 9612E	Roe H31/25R	Leeds City Transport	492	RP
EVD 406	1949	Crossley DD42/7	Roe H31/25R	Baxter's Bus Service, Airdrie	34	R
NUB 609	1950	AEC Regent III 9612E	(chassis only)	Leeds City Transport	609	A
LYR 533	1951	AEC Regent III O961 RT	Park Royal H30/26R	London Transport	RT 3314	R
JWU 886	1951	Bristol LL5G	ECW B39R	West Yorkshire Road Car Co	SGL16	R
NHN 128	1951	Bristol LL6B	ECW DP33R	United Automobile Services	BBE1	
HKW 82	1952	AEC Regent III 9613E	East Lancashire Coachbuilders H31/28R	Bradford Corporation	82	R
PJX 43	1952	Leyland Titan PD2/37	Weymann H36/28F	Halifax Corporation	43	RP
LWR 424	1953	Bristol KSW6G	ECW	West Yorkshire Road Car Co	4044	A
AEK 514	1953	Leyland Royal Tiger PSU1/13	Northern Counties B44F	Wigan Corporation	101	A
SVS 904	1954	Bristol LS6G	ECW C35F	Southern National Omnibus Co	1381	R
JVH 381	1955	AEC Regent III 9613E	East Lancashire Coachbuilders H35/28R	Huddersfield Corporation	181	A
PGK 872	1955	Bedford SBG	Mulliner B30F	Ministry of Supply		A
UUA 214	1955	Leyland Titan PD2/11	Roe H33/25R	Leeds City Transport	214	RP
XLG 477	1956	Atkinson Alpha PL745H	Northern Counties B34C	SHMD Board	77	A
GJX 331	1956	Daimler CVG6	Roe H37/26R	Halifax Corporation	119	R
VTU 76	1956	Daimler CVG6	Northern Counties H35/23C	SHMD Board	76	RP
SYG 561	1957	Bedford SBG	Duple C41F	Walton & Helliwell, Mytholmroyd		A
KAG 856	1957	Leyland Titan PD2/20	Alexander L31/28R	Western SMT Co	1375	RP
DHD 177	1959	AEC Regent V 2LD3RA	MCW H39/31F	Yorkshire Woollen District Transport Co	797	A
RCP 237	1962	AEC Regent V 2D3RA	Northern Counties H39/32F	Hebble Motor Services	619	A
PJX 232	1962	Leyland Leopard L1	Weymann B44F	Halifax Joint Omnibus Committee	232	R
WBR 246	1963	Atkinson Alpha PM746HL	Marshall B45D	Sunderland Corporation	46	RP
6220 KW	1964	AEC Regent V 2D3RA	MCW H40/30F	Bradford Corporation	220	R
TRN 731	1964	Leyland Leopard PSU3/3R	Plaxton C49F	Ribble Motor Services	7315	R

39

Registration	Date	Chassis	Body	New to	Fleet No	Status
ENW 980D	1966	AEC Regent V 2D2RA	Roe H39/31R	Leeds City Transport	980	RP
KWT 642D	1966	Bristol Lodekka FS6B	ECW H33/27RD	West Yorkshire Road Car Co	DX210	R
NWU 265D	1966	Bristol Lodekka FS6B	ECW H33/27RD	West Yorkshire Road Car Co	YDX221	A
HNW 131D	1966	Daimler Fleetline CRG6LX	Roe H45/33F	Leeds City Transport	131	R
KVH 473E	1966	Daimler Fleetline CRG6LX	Roe H44/31F	Huddersfield Corporation	473	R
TWW 766F	1967	Bristol RELH6G	ECW C47F	West Yorkshire Road Car Co	CRG6	R
YLG 717F	1967	Bristol RESL6G	Northern Counties B43F	SHMD Board	117	A
LAK 309G	1969	Leyland Titan PD3A/12	Alexander H41/29F	Bradford Corporation	309	R
OWY 750K	1972	Bristol RESL6G	ECW B33D	Keighley-West Yorkshire Services	2109	A
XAK 355L	1972	Daimler Fleetline CRL6	Alexander H43/31F	Bradford Corporation	355	RP
WFM 801K	1972	Leyland National 1151/2R/0403	Leyland National B49F	Crosville Motor Services	SNL801	R
OWT 776M	1974	Bristol RELL6G	ECW B53F	West Yorkshire Road Car Co	1403	R
MUA 45P	1976	Bristol LHS6L	ECW DP27F	West Yorkshire PTE	45	A
MUA 870P	1976	Leyland Atlantean AN68/1R	Roe H43/30F	Yorkshire Woollen District Transport Co	773	R
PUH 149W +Trolleybus	1980	Bristol VRT/SL3	ECW H43/31F	West Yorkshire Road Car Co	1746	A

Notes:

WT 7101	Solid tyres
TF 6860	Used as a tow bus and snow plough 1950-1963
CWX 671	Rebodied 1950
EUF 198	Converted to a towing vehicle from bus 198 in 1957
RN 8622	Chassis refurbished and rebodied in 1949
FWX 914	rebodied 1963
NNW 492	Leeds City Transport driver trainer 1968-1971
EVD 406	New with Scottish Commercial body; acquired by J Wood & Son, Mirfield, in 1953 and rebodied 1955
LWR 424	Originally bus 858 (later DGW4); converted to a towing vehicle and renumbered 4044 in 1972

SVS 904	Originally registered OTT 90
UUA 214	Leeds City Transport driver trainer 1972-1978
KWT 642D	Renumbered 1810 in 1971
NWU 265D	Renumbered 3821 in 1971
TWW 766F	Renumbered 1019 in 1971; restored in later guise as 2508
OWY 750K	Originally B44F
WFM 801K	Second production Leyland National, delivered as B44D; converted to single door by Greater Manchester Buses (South)
OWT 776M	Delivered with Leyland O680 engine

Restored Royal Blue coaches from the half-cab era are rare. Western National 1228, a 1948 Beadle-bodied Bristol L6A is currently to be found at Keighley Bus Museum. *Philip Lamb*

Contact address: Whisby Road, North Hykeham, Lincoln LN6 3QT
Phone: 01522 689497
Fax: 01522 689292
Web site: www.lvvs.freeserve.co.uk
Affiliation: NARTM
Brief description: An impressive collection of over 50 vehicles including classic cars, commercials, buses and motor cycles, mostly with Lincolnshire connections. Sixty years of road transport history is represented in the museum hall, which was built in 1993.
Events planned: Open days on 15 April 2001, 4 Nov 2001
Opening days/times: May to October: Monday to Friday 12.00 to 16.00; Sunday 10.00 to 16.00;

November to April: Sunday 12.00 to 17.00. Other times by appointment
Directions by car: Just off A46 Lincoln by-pass on Whisby Road, which links A46 to B1190.
Directions by public transport:
1 mile from North Hykeham railway station.
Whisby Road is just off Doddington Road, served by several bus routes.
Charges: No charge but donations welcome.
Facilities: A B(e) D P T
Other information: Refreshments available on open days.

Registration	Date	Chassis	Body	New to	Fleet No	Status
KW 474	1927	Leyland Lion PLSC1	Leyland B31F	Blythe & Berwick, Bradford	-	R
TE 8318	1929	Chevrolet LQ	Spicer C14D	Jardine, Morcambe	-	R
VL 1263	1929	Leyland Lion LT1	Applewhite B32R	Lincoln Corporation	5	R
WH 1553	1929	Leyland Titan TD1	Leyland L27/24RO	Bolton Corporation	54	R
KW 7604	1930	Leyland Badger TA4	Plaxton B20F	Bradford Education Committee	023	R
TF 818	1930	Leyland Lion LT1	Roe B30F	Lancashire United Transport	202	R
FW 5698	1935	Leyland Tiger TS7	Burlingham B35F	Lincolnshire Road Car Co	1411	R
RC 2721	1935	SOS DON	Brush B—F	Trent Motor Traction Co	321	R
FHN 833	1940	Bristol L5G	ECW B35F	United Automobile Services	BLO133	RP
BFE 419	1941	Leyland Titan TD7	Roe H30/26R	Lincoln Corporation	64	R
DBE 187	1946	Bristol K6A	ECW H30/26R	Lincolnshire Road Car Co	2115	RP
AHE 163	1946	Leyland Titan PD1	Roe H31/25R	Yorkshire Traction	726	RP
DFE 383	1948	Guy Arab III	Guy H30/26R	Lincoln Corporation	23	R
HPW 133	1949	Bristol K5G	ECW H30/26R	Eastern Counties Omnibus Co	LKH 133	R
ONO 59	1949	Bristol K5G	ECW	Eastern National Omnibus Co	4038	R
OHK 432	1949	Daimler CVD6	Roberts H30/26R	Colchester Corporation	4	R
FFU 860	1950	AEC Regal III 9621E	Willowbrook DP35F	Enterprise, Scunthorpe	60	R
LTB 907	1950	Bedford OB	Duple C29F	Penn, Warrington	-	R
FDO 573	1953	AEC Regent III 9613E	Willowbrook H32/28RD	J W Camplin & Sons ('Holme Delight'), Donington	-	R
OLD 714	1954	AEC Regent III O961 RT	Weymann H30/26R	London Transport	RT 4494	R
LFW 326	1955	Bristol Lodekka LD6B	ECW H33/25RD	Lincolnshire Road Car Co	2318	R
RFE 416	1961	Leyland Titan PD2/41	Roe H33/28R	Lincoln Corporation	89	R
952 JUB	1964	AEC Regent V 2D2RA	Roe H39/31R	Leeds City Transport	952	R
EVL 549E	1967	Leyland Panther PSUR1/1R	Roe DP45F	Lincoln Corporation	41	RP

Notes:

KW 474	Restored as Lincoln Corporation No 1	
FW 5698	Rebodied 1949	
FNH 833	Later renumbered BG147	
DFE 383	Ruston Hornsby air cooled engine	
ONO 59	Renumbered 1427 in 1954 and 2255 in 1964; subsequently converted to caravan	
FFU 860	Passed to Lincolnshire Road Car Co (860) in 1950	

Contact address: 39 Wellington Street, London WC2E 7BB.
Phone: 0207 379 6344; recorded information 0207 565 7299
E-mail: website: www.ltmuseum.co.uk
Affiliation: NARTM
Brief description: Travel through time at the London Transport Museum. It's London's history. It's London's people. It's trams, trains, buses and more. It's a hands-on moving experience right in the heart of London at Covent Garden.
Opening days/times: Daily 10.00 to 18.00 (Fri 11.00 to 18.00) Last admission 17.15. Closed 24, 25 and 26 December.

Directions by car: Limited parking at parking meters in Covent Garden, Holborn/Kingsway area.
Directions by public transport:
Buses to Strand or Aldwych: 4, 11, 15, 23, 26, 76, 172 and 341. Underground to Covent Garden, Leicester Square or Holborn.
Charges: Adult £5.50, Concession £2.95, under 16s free, other prices available — contact the Museum for details. For school rates please telephone Resource Centre.
Facilities: A C D F G H L R S T

Registration	Date	Chassis	Body	New to	Fleet No	Status
note m	1829	Horse bus	London General Omnibus Co	George Shillibeer		R
note n	1875	Horse bus	Thomas Tilling -24-	Thomas Tilling		R
note p	1888	Horse bus	London General Omnibus Co -26-	London General Omnibus Co		R
LC 3701	1906	De Dion	(chassis only)	London General Omnibus Co	L7	R
LA 9928	1911	LGOC B	London General Omnibus Co O18/16RO	London General Omnibus Co	B340	R
XC 8059	1921	AEC K	London General Omnibus Co O24/22RO	London General Omnibus Co	K424	R
XM 7399	1923	AEC S	London General Omnibus Co O28/26RO	London General Omnibus Co	S742	R
MN 2615	1923	Tilling Stevens TS3A Petrol Electric	(chassis only)	Douglas Corporation	10	R
YR 3844	1926	AEC NS	London General Omnibus Co H28/24RO	London General Omnibus Co	NS1995	R
HX 2756+	1931	AEC 663T	UCC H32/24R	London United Tramways	1	R
GK 5486	1931	AEC Regal 662	Duple C30F	London General Omnibus Co	T219	R
GK 3192	1931	AEC Regent 661	London General Omnibus Co H28/20R	London General Omnibus Co	ST821	R
GK 5323	1931	AEC Renown 663	London General Omnibus Co H33/23R	London General Omnibus Co	LT165	R
GO 5198	1931	AEC Renown 664	London General Omnibus Co B—F	London General Omnibus Co	LT1076	RP
AXM 649	1934	AEC Regent 661	Chalmers	London Transport	STL43	R
AYV 651	1934	AEC Regent 661	LPTB H30/26R	London Transport	STL469	R
BXD 576	1935	AEC Q O762	Birmingham R C & W B35C	London Transport	Q55	R
CLE 122	1936	Leyland Cub KP03	Weymann B20F	London Transport	C94	R
FJJ 774	1939	Leyland FEC	LPTB B34F	London Transport	TF77	R
EXV 253+	1939	Leyland LPTB70	Leyland H40/30R	London Transport	1253	R
HYM 768+	1948	BUT 9641T	Metro Cammell H40/30R	London Transport	1768	R
NLE 537	1953	AEC Regal IV 9821LT RF	Metro Cammell B39F	London Transport	RF537	R
MXX 364	1953	Guy Special NLLVP	ECW B26F	London Transport	GS64	R
NXP 997	1954	AEC Regent III O961 RT	Park Royal H30/26R	London Transport	RT4712	R
OLD 589	1954	AEC Regent III O961 RT	Park Royal H30/26R	London Transport	RT4825	R
SLT 56	1956	AEC Routemaster	Park Royal/LTE H36/28R	London Transport	RM1	R
SLT 57	1957	AEC Routemaster	Park Royal/LTE H36/28R	London Transport	RM2	R
737 DYE	1963	AEC Routemaster 2R2RH	Park Royal H36/28R	London Transport	RM1737	R
CUV 229C	1965	AEC Routemaster R2RH/1	Park Royal H36/29RD	London Transport	RCL2229	R
KGY 4D	1966	AEC Routemaster FR2R	Park Royal H41/31F	London Transport	FRM1	RP
AML 582H	1969	AEC Merlin 4P2R	MCW B25D	London Transport	MBA582	R
EGP 1J	1970	Daimler Fleetline CRG6LXB	Park Royal H44/24D	London Transport	DMS1	R
KJD 401P	1976	Bristol LH6L	ECW B39F	London Transport	BL1	RP
NUW 567Y	1982	Leyland Titan TNLXB/2RR	Leyland H44/24D	London Transport	T567	RP

Registration	Date	Chassis	Body	New to	Fleet No	Status
C526 DYT	1986	Volkswagen LT55	Optare B25F	London Transport	OV2	R
note r	1993	Optare Metrorider	Optare B26F	London Transport	MRL242	R
+ Trolleybus						

Notes:

note m	Unregistered reconstruction		SLT 56	New 9/1954. First Registered 1/1956.
note n	Unregistered		SLT 57	New 1955. First Registered 5/1957.
note p	Unregistered; garden Seat type		note r	Unregistered sectioned exhibit built especially for LT
AXM 649	Rebuilt with Breakdown Vehicle body, 1950			Museum
HYM 768	Trolleybus; on display at East Anglia Transport Museum			

Manchester Museum of Transport   Cheetham

Contact address: Boyle Street, Cheetham, Manchester M8 8UL
Phone/Fax: 0161 205 2122
E-mail: gmts.enquire@btinternet.com
Web site: www.gmts.co.uk
Affiliation: NARTM
Brief description:
The museum houses over 70 buses and coaches from the Greater Manchester area, from an 1870 horse bus to a 1990 Metrolink tram. Travel back to a time of twopenny singles and coach trips to Blackpool. Extensive displays of photos, uniforms and models complement the vehicles, and visitors may enter many of the vehicles and view the museum's workshop.
Events planned:
24/25 March 2001 — Spring Transport Festival
12/13 May 2001 — A Tale of Two Cities, Manchester Weekend
16/17 June 2001 — Accessible Transport Weekend
2 September 2001 — Trans-Lancs Historic Vehicle Rally

9 September 2001 — 2001 Heritage Open Weekend
20/21 October 2001 — A Tale of Two Cities, Salford Weekend
1/2 December 2001 — Christmas Cracker Festival
Opening days/times: Wednesdays, Saturdays, Sundays & Bank Holidays: 10.00 to 17.00 (please 'phone for Christmas/New Year opening).
Directions by car:
From M62/M60 junction 18, follow 'Castlefields' signs to Cheetham Hill; from City, follow A665 (Cheetham Hill Road) — Museum signposted.
Directions by public transport:
Bus 135 or 59 to Queen's Road; Metrolink tram to Woodlands Road (10min walk).
Charges: £3.00 adult, £1.75 concession, £9 family. Season tickets available.
Facilities: B(e) C D F G H P R S T
Other information: Archives available for study by arrangement.

Registration	Date	Chassis	Body	New to	Fleet No	Status
note b	1876	Horse bus	Manchester Carriage Co. O18/14RO	Manchester Carriage Co	2	R
DB 5070	1925	Tilling Stevens TS6	Brush O54RO	North Western Road Car Co	170	R
CK 3825	1927	Leyland Lion PLSC1	Leyland B31F	Ribble Motor Services	295	R
VM 4439	1928	Leyland Tiger TS1	Metro Cammell/Crossley B32R	Manchester Corporation	138	A
VY 957	1929	Leyland Lion PLSC1	Ribble B32R	York Corporation	2	R
VR 5742	1930	Leyland Tiger TS2	Manchester Corporation Car Works B30R	Manchester Corporation	28	R
AXJ 857	1934	Leyland Titan TD3	(chassis only)	Manchester Corporation	526	R
JA 7585	1935	Leyland Tiger TS7	English Electric B35C	Stockport Corporation	185	A
RN 7824	1936	Leyland Cheetah LZ2	Brush C31F	Ribble Motor Services	1568	RP
EFJ 92	1938	Bedford WTB	Heaver C25F	Taylor, Exeter	-	RP
BBA 560	1939	AEC Regent 0661	Park Royal H26/22R	Salford Corporation	235	RP
AJA 152	1939	Bristol K5G	Willowbrook L27/26R	North Western Road Car Co	432	R
JP 4712	1940	Leyland Titan TD7	Leyland L27/26R	Wigan Corporation	70	RP
BJA 425	1946	Bristol L5G	Willowbrook B38R	North Western Road Car Co	270	R
HTB 656	1946	Leyland Tiger PS1	Roe B35R	Ramsbottom Corporation	17	R
HTF 586	1947	Bedford OB	Scottish Motor Traction C29F	Warburton Bros, Bury		R

Registration	Date	Chassis	Body	New to	Fleet No	Status
JND 791	1948	Crossley DD42/8S	Crossley H32/26R	Manchester Corporation	2150	R
CDB 224	1948	Leyland Titan PD2/1	Leyland L27/26R	North Western Road Car Co	224	R
CWH 717	1948	Leyland Titan PD2/4	Leyland -	Bolton Corporation	367	R
LMA 284	1949	Foden PVSC6	Lawton C35F	Copenall, Camberbach		R
JNA 467	1949	Leyland Titan PD1/3	Metro Cammell H32/26R	Manchester Corporation	3166	RP
BEN 177	1950	AEC Regent III 9613A	Weymann H30/26R	Bury Corporation	177	R
LTC 774+	1950	Crossley Empire TDD42/2	Crossley H30/26R	Ashton-under-Lyne Corporation	80	RP
CWG 206	1950	Leyland Tiger PS1	Alexander C35F	W Alexander & Sons	PA164	R
MTB 848	1950	Leyland Tiger PS2/1	East Lancashire Coachbuilders B35R	Rawtenstall Corporation	55	RP
HDK 835	1951	AEC Regent III 9612E	East Lancashire Coachbuilders H31/26R	Rochdale Corporation	235	RP
EDB 575	1951	Crossley DD42/7	Crossley H30/26R	Stockport Corporation	321	R
JVU 775+	1951	Crossley Dominion TDD64/1	Crossley H36/30R	Manchester Corporation	1250	R
EDB 549	1951	Leyland Titan PD2/1	Leyland O30/20R	Stockport Corporation	295	R
EDB 562	1951	Leyland Titan PD2/1	Leyland H30/26R	Stockport Corporation	308	R
JND 646	1951	Leyland Titan PD2/3	Metro Cammell H32/26R	Manchester Corporation	3245	R
NNB 125	1953	Leyland Royal Tiger PSU1/13	Northern Counties B41C	Manchester Corporation	25	R
UTC 672	1954	AEC Regent III 9613S	East Lancashire Coachbuilders L27/28RD	Bamber Bridge Motor Services	4	R
UMA 370	1955	Atkinson PD746	Northern Counties H35/24C	SHMD Board	70	R
NDK 980	1956	AEC Regent V D2RA6G	Weymann H33/28R	Rochdale Corporation	280	R
PND 460	1956	Leyland Titan PD2/12	Metro Cammell H36/28R	Manchester Corporation	3460	R
JBN 153	1956	Leyland Titan PD2/13	Metro Cammell H34/28R	Bolton Corporation	77	R
NBU 494	1957	Leyland Titan PD2/20	Roe H31/29R	Oldham Corporation	394	R
DJP 754	1957	Leyland Titan PD2/30	Northern Counties H33/28R	Wigan Corporation	115	R
116 JTD	1958	Guy Arab IV	Northern Counties H41/32R	Lancashire United Transport	21	R
122 JTD	1958	Guy Arab IV	Northern Counties H41/32R	Lancashire United Transport	27	R
TNA 520	1958	Leyland Titan PD2/34	Burlingham H37/28R	Manchester Corporation	3520	R
TNA 496	1958	Leyland Titan PD2/40	Burlingham H37/28R	Manchester Corporation	3496	R
YDK 590	1960	AEC Reliance 2MU3RA	Harrington C37F	Yelloway Motor Services, Rochdale	-	R
HEK 705	1961	Leyland Titan PD3A/2	Massey H41/29F	Wigan Corporation	57	R
TRJ 112	1962	Daimler CVG6	Metro Cammell H37/28R	Salford City Transport	112	R
414 CLT	1963	AEC Routemaster 2R2RH	Park Royal H36/28R	London Transport	RM 1414	R
4632 VM	1963	Daimler CVG6K	Metro Cammell H37/28R	Manchester Corporation	4632	R
REN 116	1963	Leyland Atlantean PDR1/1	Metro Cammell H41/33F	Bury Corporation	116	R
8860 VR	1964	AEC Regent V 2D3RA	East Lancashire Neepsend H41/32R	A Mayne & Son, Manchester		R
PTC 114C	1965	AEC Renown 3B3RA	East Lancashire Coachbuilders H41/31F	Leigh Corporation	15	R
DDB 174C	1965	Daimler Fleetline CRG6LX	Alexander H44/31F	North Western Road Car Co	174	R
DBA 214C	1965	Leyland Atlantean PDR1/1	Metro Cammell H43/33F	Salford Corporation	214	RP
BND 874C	1965	Leyland Panther Cub PSURC1/1	Park Royal B43D	Manchester Corporation	74	R
PTE 944C	1965	Leyland Titan PD2/37	Roe H37/28F	Ashton-under-Lyne Corporation	44	R
FRJ 254D	1966	Leyland Titan PD2/40	Metro Cammell H36/28F	Salford City Transport	254	R
JRJ 281E	1967	Leyland Titan PD2/40	Metro Cammell H36/28F	Salford City Transport	281	R
HVM 901F	1968	Leyland Atlantean PDR1/1	Park Royal H45/28D	Manchester City Transport	1001	R
KDB 408F	1968	Leyland Leopard PSU4/1R	East Lancashire Coachbuilders B43D	Stockport Corporation	408	RP
KJA 871F	1968	Leyland Titan PD3/14	East Lancashire Coachbuilders H38/32R	Stockport Corporation	71	R
MJA 891G	1969	Leyland Titan PD3/14	East Lancashire Coachbuilders H38/32R	Stockport Corporation	91	R
MJA 897G	1969	Leyland Titan PD3/14	East Lancashire Coachbuilders O38/32F	Stockport Corporation	97	R
TTD 386H	1969	Leyland Titan PD3/14	East Lancashire Coachbuilders H41/32F	Ramsbottom Corporation	11	R
VNB 101L	1972	Leyland Atlantean AN68/1R	Park Royal H43/32F	SELNEC PTE	7001	R
TXJ 507K	1972	Leyland National 1151/2R/0202	Leyland National B46D	SELNEC PTE	EX30	R

Above: 1960 Harrington-bodied AEC Reliance YDK 590 is one of two Yelloway Coaches preserved at the Manchester Museum of Transport. *Philip Lamb*

Below: Seen outside the Manchester Museum of Transport is Lancashire United 27, one of a pair of similar Northern Counties Guy Arab IVs preserved there. *Philip Lamb*

Registration	Date	Chassis	Body	New to	Fleet No	Status
XVU 352M	1973	Seddon Pennine IV-236	Seddon B19F	SELNEC PTE	1722	A
HVU 244N	1975	AEC Reliance 6U3ZR	Plaxton C49F	Yelloway Motor Services, Rochdale		R
GNC 276N	1975	Seddon Lucas	Seddon B19F	Greater Manchester PTE	EX62	R
ORJ 83W	1981	MCW Metrobus DR102/21	MCW H43/30F	Greater Manchester PTE	5083	A
A706 LNC	1984	Leyland Atlantean AN68D/1R	Northern Counties H43/32F	Greater Manchester PTE	8706	A
D63 NOF	1986	Freight Rover 400 Special	Carlyle B18F	Manchester Minibuses (Bee Line Buzz Co.)	-	A

+ Trolleybus

Notes:

note b	Largest surviving horse bus.	UMA 370	Only Atkinson double-decker bodied. Originally H35/25C.
DB 5070	Petrol Electric transmission		
CK 3825	Body rebuilt 1981	414 CLT	Loaned to Manchester Corporation when new, Feb 1963.
VM 4439	Body new 1935		
VY 957	Body rebuilt 1983; restored to Ribble livery	HVM 901F	First 'Mancunian' double-decker
VR 5742	Rebodied 1937	TTD 386H	Last half-cab double-decker delivered to a British operator
AJA 152	Rebodied 1951		
BJA 425	Originally numbered 125; rebodied 1958 with 1952 body	MJA 891G	Last open-rear-platform double-decker delivered to a British operator
CWH 717	Originally H30/26R; converted to tower wagon 1963.	MJA 897G	Originally H38/32F; converted to open-top in 1982
LMA 284	Body new 1954	VNB 101L	First SELNEC Standard double-decker
EDB 562	Used as training bus, 1968-1978	TXJ 507K	First production Leyland National
EDB 549	Originally H30/26R	GNC 276N	Battery- powered

Greengate, adjacent to Manchester Victoria station was until recently a bus terminal. There we find the Manchester Museum of Transport's Bury 177, a 1950 Weymann-bodied AEC Regent III. *Philip Lamb*

Museum of British Road Transport — Coventry

Contact address: Hales Street, Coventry CV1 1PN
Phone: 024 7683 2425
Fax: 024 7683 2465
E-mail: museum@mbrt.co.uk
Brief description: The museum has over 210 cars and commercial vehicles, over 90 motorcycles and around 240 bicycles. Various tableaux chart the development of the motor vehicle from the early years, and Coventry's contribution to this can be seen in the many marques on display. Other exhibits include a 633mph land speed record car, several thousand die-cast models and a walk through audio visual display of the Coventry Blitz experience.

Events planned: Please see the enthusiast press for details.
Opening days/times: Seven days a week, 10.00 to 17.00 (except Christmas Eve, Christmas Day and Boxing Day.)
Directions by car: Follow brown 'Motor Museum' signs from Coventry City Centre.
Directions by public transport: Museum is close to Pool Meadow bus station; use bus 17 or 27 from Coventry railway station to Pool Meadow.
Charges: Free admission
Facilities: A D F G H L R S T

Registration	Date	Chassis	Body	New to	Fleet No	Status
Note t	1916	Maudslay	no body			A
EKV 966	1944	Daimler CWA6	Roe H31/25R	Coventry Corporation	366	R
JNB 416	1948	Maudslay Marathon II	Trans-United C33F	Hackett's, Manchester		R
KOM 150	1950	Daimler CVD6	Wilsdon -	Birmingham Post and Mail		R
SRB 424	1953	Daimler CD650	Willowbrook L27/28RD	Tailby & George ('Blue Bus Services'), Willington		R
PBC 734	1954	Karrier Bantam Q25	Reading C14F	Mablethorpe Homes, Leicester	-	R
333 CRW	1963	Daimler CVG6	Metro Cammell H34/29R	Coventry Corporation	333	R
PDU 125M	1973	Daimler Fleetline CRG6LX	East Lancashire Coachbuilders O44/30F	Coventry Corporation	125	R

Notes:

Note t	To be restored as replica of 1921 Hickman bodied bus for Coventry Corporation	KOM 150	Currently used as museum promotional vehicle
		PBC 734	Welfare bus
EKV 966	Rebodied 1951; converted to mobile repair workshop (O2) in 1960	PDU 125M	Originally H44/30F; converted to open top in 1986

Museum of Transport — Glasgow

Contact address: Kelvin Hall, 1 Bunhouse Road, Glasgow G3 8DP
Phone: 0141 287 2720 (school bookings on 0141 287 2747)
Fax: 0141 287 2692
Affiliation: NARTM
Brief description: The museum displays many items of transport history dating from the 1870s.
Opening days/times: Monday to Saturday, 10.00 to 17.00; Sunday 11.00 to 17.00 (closed 25/26 December and 1/2 January).

Directions by car: From M8 junctions 17 or 19.
Directions by public transport: Bus from City Centre (Dumbarton Road) to Kelvin Hall; Underground to Kelvin Hall; nearest main-line railway station is Partick.
Charges: Free admission
Facilities: D F G H R T
Other information: Guided tours and exhibitions also held.

Registration	Date	Chassis	Body	New to	Fleet No	Status
EGA 79	1949	Albion Venturer CX 37S	Croft H30/26R	Glasgow Corporation	B92	R
FYS 988+	1958	BUT RETB1	Burlingham B50F	Glasgow Corporation	TBS13	R
FYS 998	1958	Leyland Atlantean PDR1/1	Alexander H44/34F	Glasgow Corporation	LA1	R
+Trolleybus						

Notes:

FYS 988	Exhibited at the 1958 Commercial Motor Show

Contact address: Exhibition Road, London SW7 2DD
Phone: 0207 942 4209
E-mail: k.shirt@nmsi.ac.uk
Brief description: The bus collection is located at Wroughton airfield (hangar 4), near Swindon, Wiltshire.
Events planned: Open days are held and details of these may be found in the enthusiast press.

Opening days/times: Open only on Transport Festival and Open Days.
Directions by car: On A4361 approx 4 miles south of Swindon.
Directions by public transport: Publicised for Open Days
Charges: Published for each event.

Registration	Date	Chassis	Body	New to	Fleet No	Status
LMJ 653G	1913	Fiat 52B		(operator unknown) Yugoslavia		RP
JCP 60F	1928	Leyland Lion PLSC1	Leyland B31F	Jersey Railways & Tramways		A
DR 4902	1929	Leyland Titan TD1	Leyland L51RO	National Omnibus & Transport Co	2849	A
DX 8871+	1930	Ransomes Simms & Jefferies D	Ransomes Simms & Jefferies B31D	Ipswich Corporation	44	A
VO 6806	1931	AEC Regal 662	Cravens B32F	Red Bus, Mansfield		A
GW 713	1931	Gilford 1680T	Weymann C30D	Vallient, Ealing		A
JN 5783	1935	AEC Q 762	(chassis only)	Westcliff-on-Sea Motor Services		A
CPM 61+	1939	AEC 661T	Weymann H28/26R	Brighton Hove & District Omnibus Co	6340	A
FR 1347	1940	Saurer CRD		GFM (Switzerland)	52	A
DHR 192	1943	Guy Arab II	Weymann UH30/26R	Swindon Corporation	51	A
KPT 909	1949	Leyland Titan PD2/1	Leyland L27/26R	Weardale Motor Services, Frosterley		R
LTA 772	1951	Bristol LWL5G	ECW B32R	Western National Omnibus Co	1613	A
NLP 645	1953	AEC Regal IV 9822E	Park Royal RDP37C	British European Airways	1035	A
OTT 55	1953	Bristol LS5G	ECW B41F	Southern National Omnibus Co	1701	A
HET 513	1953	Crossley DD42/7	Crossley H30/26R	Rotherham Corporation	213	A
OLJ 291	1954	Bedford CAV	Bedford B12	Non-psv use		A
VLT 140	1960	AEC Routemaster R2RH	Park Royal H36/28R	London Transport	RM140	R
504 EBL	1963	Bedford VAL 14	Duple C52F	Reliance Motor Services, Newbury	87	A
note u	1970	Moulton MD	Moulton C23F	Moulton Development vehicle		A
BCD 820L	1973	Leyland National 1151/1R/0102	Leyland National B49F	Southdown Motor Services	20	A
+ Trolleybus						

Notes:
LMJ 653G   Yugoslavia
JCP 60F   Originally registered J 4601
FR 1347   Displays original Swiss registration FR1347
note u   Eight wheeled integral development vehicle (unregistered)

The Science Museum Collection at Wroughton, near Swindon is home to 1953 all-Crossley DD42/7, Rotherham 213 and on the right, London Transport RM140, an AEC Routemaster built in 1960.
Philip Lamb

North of England Open Air Museum   Beamish

Contact address: Beamish, Co Durham, DH9 0RG
Phone: 01207 231811
Fax: 01207 290933
E-mail: Beamish@neoam.demon.co.uk
Brief description: Beamish is an open-air museum which vividly recreates life in the North of England in the 19th and early 20th century. Buildings from throughout the region have been brought to Beamish, rebuilt and furnished as they once were. Costumed staff welcome visitors and demonstrate the past way of life in The Town, Colliery Village, Home Farm, Railway Station, Pockerley Manor and 1825 Railway. A one-mile circular period tramway carries visitors around the Museum and a replica 1913 Daimler bus operates between The Town and Colliery Village.

Events planned: —
13 to 16 April 2001 — The History of Meccano
10 June 2001 — Morgan car meet
1/2 September 2001 — Vintage collections weekend
23 September 2001 — Classic car day

Opening days/times:
Summer: 7 April to 28 October: 10.00 to 17.00 (open every day)
Winter 29 October to 22 March 2002: 10.00 to 16.00 (closed Mondays and Fridays); closed 10 December to 1 January (inclusive). Reduced operations in winter.
Last admission always 15.00.
Directions by car: Follow A1(M) to junction 63 (Chester-le-Street exit). Take A693 towards Stanley and follow Beamish Museum signs.
Directions by public transport: Buses 709 from Newcastle, 720 from Durham and 775/778 from Sunderland all serve Beamish.
Charges: --
Summer: Adult £12, Child £6, Over 60s £9.
Winter: £4 per person.
Group rates available for parties of 20 or more (not winter).
Facilities: B E F G H M P R T
Other information: Beamish is not ideal for wheelchair users. Free leaflet available in advance for visitors with disabilities and mobility limitations.

Registration	Date	Chassis	Body	New to	Fleet No	Status
WT 7108+	1924	Straker Clough T29	Brush B32F	Keighley Corporation Tramways	12	A
UP 551	1928	SOS QL	Brush Replica B37F	Northern General Transport	338	RP
VK 5401	1931	Dodge UF30A	Robson, Consett B14F"	Baty, Rookhope		A
LTN 501+	1948	Sunbeam S7	Northern Coach Builders H39/31R	Newcastle Corporation	501	R
J 2503	1988	Renault	Osborne O18/14RO	Beamish, the North of England Open Air Museum		R

+Trolleybus

Notes:
UP 551	Replica body in the course of construction
J 2503	Replica of 1913 Daimler.

The North of England Open Air Museum is home to Newcastle 501, a Northern Coach Builders-bodied Sunbeam S7, dating from 1948.
Stephen Morris

Contact address: Mere Way, Ruddington, Nottingham NG11 6NX
Phone: 0115 940 5705
E-mail: aecley@aol.co
Affiliation: NARTM
Brief description: The centre offers exhibits covering road and rail transport along with steam road vehicles, and provides the opportunity to experience travel of a bygone age.
Events planned: 26/27 May, 5 August, 9 September, 14 October.

Opening days/times: 1 April to 14 October: Sundays and Bank Holiday Mondays.
Directions by car: 3 miles south of Nottingham just off A52 ring-road and main A60 road via small roundabout at Ruddington.
Directions by public transport: Buses from Nottingham pass near museum.
Charges: Not finalised at time of publication.
Facilities: B B(e) D E G H P R S T

Registration	Date	Chassis	Body	New to	Fleet No	Status
W 963	1923	Daimler CJA	Barton Ch22	Barton Transport, Chilwell		R
VO 8846	1932	Leyland Lion LT5	Willowbrook DP32F	South Notts Bus Co, Gotham	17	A
CRR 819	1947	Leyland Cub KPZ2	Brush C20F	Barton Transport, Chilwell	284	RP
DJF 349	1947	Leyland Titan PD1	Leyland H30/26R	Leicester City Transport	248	A
JRR 930	1948	Leyland Titan PD1A	Duple L29/26F	Barton Transport, Chilwell	509	A
JVO 230	1948	Leyland Titan PD1A	Duple L29/26F	Barton Transport, Chilwell	507	R
MAL 310	1951	Leyland Royal Tiger PSU1/11	Duple DP45F	South Notts Bus Co, Gotham	42	A
OTV 161	1953	AEC Regent III 9613E	Park Royal H30/26R	Nottingham City Transport	161	R
NNN 968	1953	Leyland BTS1	Barton	Barton Transport, Chilwell	668	A
APR 167A	1953	Leyland Titan PD2/12	Leyland H30/26RD	Barton Transport, Chilwell	732	A
PFN 865	1959	AEC Regent V 2LD3RA		East Kent Road Car Co		RP
851 FNN	1960	AEC Regent V 2D3RA	Northern Counties FL37/33F	Barton Transport, Chilwell	851	R
AAL 522A	1960	AEC Regent V 2D3RA	Northern Counties FL37/33F	Barton Transport, Chilwell	854	A
861 HAL	1960	Dennis Loline II	Northern Counties FL37/31F	Barton Transport, Chilwell	861	R
YRC 194	1962	Leyland Tiger Cub PSUC1/1	Alexander DP41F	Trent Motor Traction Co	194	RP
80 NVO	1962	Leyland Titan PD3/4	Northern Counties L33/32F	South Notts Bus Co, Gotham	80	A
APA 46B	1964	AEC Reliance	Willowbrook B—F	Safeguard, Guildford		RP
CTT 518C	1965	AEC Regent V 2MD3RA	Willowbrook H33/28F	Devon General Omnibus & Touring Co	518	RP
DAU 370C	1965	AEC Renown 3B3RA	Weymann H40/30F	Nottingham City Transport	370	R
ETO 452C	1965	Leyland Atlantean PDR1/1	Metro Cammell	Nottingham City Transport	452	A
EOD 524D	1966	AEC Regent V 2D3RA	MCW H34/25F	Devon General Omnibus & Touring Co	524	R
FEL 751D	1966	Bristol MW6G	ECW C39F	Hants & Dorset Motor Services	904	R
LNN 89E	1967	Albion Lowlander LR3	Northern Counties H41/30F	South Notts Bus Co, Gotham	89	A
RCH 518F	1968	Daimler Fleetline CRG6LX	Alexander H44/33F	Trent Motor Traction Co	518	A
STO 523H	1970	Leyland Atlantean PDR1A/1	Northern Counties H47/30D	Nottingham City Transport	523	R
KVO 429P	1975	Leyland National 11351/2R	Leyland National B50F	Trent Motor Traction Co	429	A
ORC 545P	1976	Leyland Atlantean AN68/1R	ECW	Northern General Transport	3299	R
GTX 761W	1980	Bristol LHS6L	ECW DP27F	National Welsh	MD8026	RP
SCH 117X	1981	Daimler Fleetline	ECW	South Notts Bus Co, Gotham	117	R
VRC 612Y	1981	Leyland Leopard PSU3G/4R	Plaxton C53F	Barton Transport, Chilwell	612	R

Notes:

APR 167A	Originally registered RAL334	LNN 89E	Last Albion Lowlander delivered; badged 'Leyland'
PFN 865	Recovery vehicle	KVO 429P	Originally B44D
AAL 522A	Originally registered 854FNN	ORC 545P	Originally H45/27D and registered MPT299P; used as promotional vehicle
861 HAL	Carries ultra-low-height 12ft 6in body		

Contact address: Station Yard, Long Hanborough, Witney, Oxfordshire, OX8 8LA

Phone: 01993 883617 (Answerphone) or 01865 400002

Affiliation: NARTM

Brief description: Over 30 buses dating from 1915 to 1986, mainly from City of Oxford Motor Services and other local companies. The collection includes many vehicles of AEC manufacture.

Events planned: Please see enthusiast press for details.

Opening days/times: Sundays and Bank Holiday Mondays, 10.30 to 16.30. Saturdays open from Easter until the last Saturday in October, 13.30-16.30. Bus rides at 15.00 on the first Sunday of each month from the first Sunday in April to the first Sunday in October inclusive.

Directions by car: The entrance is on the south side of the A4095

(Witney-Bicester), between the villages of Bladon and Long Hanborough.

Directions by public transport: Museum is adjacent to Hanborough railway station on the Oxford-Worcester line, Sunday train services (journey time Oxford 10mins, London Paddington 70mins). Stagecoach bus service from George Street Oxford, weekdays, hourly to Long Hanborough village centre (1 mile).

Charges: Adults £2, Children/OAP £1.00, Family (2+2) £5.

Facilities: B(e) D P R S T

Other information: School parties welcome by arrangement — please telephone in advance.

Registration	Date	Chassis	Body			Body
	New to		Fleet No	Status		
DU 4838	1915	Daimler Y	City of Oxford Electric Tramways B32R	City of Oxford Electric Tramways	39	RP
note e	1916	Daimler Y	(chassis only)			A
note f	1916	Daimler Y	(chassis only)			A
FC 2602	1917	Daimler Y	O18/16RO	City of Oxford Electric Tramways	46	A
J 1418	1932	AEC Regal 642	(lorry body)	City of Oxford Motor Services	GC41	A
JO 5403	1932	AEC Regent 661	Brush O28/24R	City of Oxford Motor Services	GA16	RP
HA 8047	1933	SOS REDD	Metro Cammell H26/26R	BMMO ('Midland Red')	1047	RP
NJO 703	1949	AEC Regal III 9621A	Willowbrook DP32F	City of Oxford Motor Services	703	R
OFC 393	1949	AEC Regent III 9612A	Weymann H30/26R	City of Oxford Motor Services	H892	A
OFC 205	1950	AEC Regal III 6821A	Duple C32F	South Midland Motor Services	66	A
PWL 413	1950	AEC Regent III 9613A	Weymann L27/26R	City of Oxford Motor Services	L166	RP
SFC 609	1952	AEC Regal IV 9821S	Willowbrook C37C	City of Oxford Motor Services	609	A
SFC 610	1952	AEC Regal IV 9821S	Willowbrook C37C	City of Oxford Motor Services	610	RP
GJB 254	1952	Bristol LWL6B	ECW B39R	Thames Valley Traction Co	616	A
TWL 928	1953	AEC Regent III 9613S	Park Royal H30/26R	City of Oxford Motor Services	H928	RP
956 AJO	1957	AEC Regent V MD3RV	Park Royal H33/28R	City of Oxford Motor Services	H956	R
YNX 478	1958	AEC Reliance MU3RA	Duple Midland B44F	Chiltern Queens, Woodcote		RP
756 KFC	1960	AEC Reliance 2MU3RV	Park Royal B44F	City of Oxford Motor Services	756	R
304 KFC	1961	Dennis Loline II	East Lancashire Coachbuilders H35/28F	City of Oxford Motor Services	304	RP
305 KFC	1961	Dennis Loline II	East Lancashire Coachbuilders H35/28F	City of Oxford Motor Services	305	R
14 LFC	1961	Morris FF	Wadham C27F	Morris Motors		A
850 ABK	1962	AEC Reliance 2MU3RA	Duple C43F	Don Motor Coaches, Southsea		RP
AD 7156	1966	AEC Renown 2D2RA	Metal Sections H51/39D	Kowloon Motor Bus	A165	A
FWL 371E	1967	AEC Renown 3B3RA	Northern Counties H38/27F	City of Oxford Motor Services	371	RP
NAC 416F	1967	Leyland Atlantean PDR1A/1	Northern Counties H44/31F	Stratford-upon-Avon Blue Motors	10	RP
UFC 430K	1971	Daimler Fleetline CRL6	Northern Counties H43/27D	City of Oxford Motor Services	430	A
VER 262L	1972	AEC Reliance 2U3ZR	Alexander C53F	Premier Travel, Cambridge	262	A
EUD 256K	1972	AEC Reliance 6MU4R	Plaxton B47F	Chiltern Queens, Woodcote		A
HUD 476S	1977	Bristol VRTSL3/6LXB	ECW H43/27D	City of Oxford Motor Services	476	R
UKE 830X	1982	Leyland Leopard PSU3G/4R	ECW C49F	East Kent Road Car Co	3830	A
A869 SUL	1983	Leyland Titan TNLXB/2RRSP	Leyland H44/26D	London Buses	T869	A
B106 XJO	1985	Ford Transit	Dormobile B16F	South Midland Motor Services	SM6	RP
D122 PTT	1987	Ford Transit 190D	Mellor B16F	Thames Transit	122	R

Notes:

DU 4838	Body new 1920	J 1418	Originally registered JO 5032; passed to Mascot Motors, Jersey and subsequently converted to lorry
note e	Chassis only		
note f	Chassis only	JO 5403	Originally H28/24R
FC 2602	Body ex-London built 1906	HA 8047	Sole surviving SOS double decker

Registration	Date	Chassis	Body	New to		
YNX 478			Carries 1956 body transferred from Dennis Pelican chassis			
305 KFC			Sectioned museum display, showing body construction method			
14 LFC			Originally used for Morris Motors band			
850 ABK			Acquired by Chiltern Queens, Woodcote in 1964			

AD 7156	Hong Kong registration
NAC 416F	Acquired by City of Oxford Motor Services (905) in 1970
A869 SUL	Acquired by City of Oxford Motor Services (975) in 1993

St Helens Transport Museum

Contact address: The Old Bus Depot, 51 Hall Street, St Helens, WA10 1DU
Phone: 01744 451681
E-mail: E-mail@sthelens-transport-museum.co.uk
website: www.sthelens-transport-museum.co.uk
Affiliation: NARTM
Brief description: A collection of over 100 historic vehicles representing the transport heritage of the northwest of England.

There is also a small exhibits section containing ticket machines, uniforms, signs and other transport-related items.
Events planned: Please see the enthusiast press for details
Opening days/times: Currently closed pending roof repairs; reopening will be publicised in the enthusiast press and on the St Helens website.
Facilities: A B(e) D G T

Registration	Date	Chassis	Body	New to	Fleet No	Status
ED 6141	1930	Leyland Titan TD1	Massey H28/26R	Warrington Corporation	22	A
KR 1728	1930	Leyland Titan TD1	Short H48R	Maidstone & District Motor Services	321	A
KJ 2578	1931	Leyland Titan TD1	Weymann	Redcar Motor Services, Tunbridge Well		A
AFY 971	1934	Leyland Titan TD3	English Electric O26/25R	Southport Corporation	43	A
ATD 683	1935	Leyland Lion LT7	Massey B30R	Widnes Corporation	39	A
RV 6360	1935	Leyland Titan TD4	English Electric O26/24R	Portsmouth Corporation	117	R
FTB 11	1942	Leyland Titan TD7	Northern Coach Builders UL27/26R	Leigh Corporation	84	A
EWM 358	1945	Daimler CWA6	Duple UH30/26R	Southport Corporation	62	A
DKY 713+	1945	Karrier W	East Lancashire Coachbuilders H37/29F	Bradford Corporation	713	A
ANQ 778	1946	AEC Regent III	Commonwealth Engineering	Dept of Road Transport & Tramways, Sydney	1984	A
HLW 159	1946	AEC Regent III O961 RT	Park Royal H30/26R	London Transport	RT 172	R
DED 797	1946	Leyland Titan PD1	Alexander H30/26R	Warrington Corporation	16	A
ARN 392	1946	Leyland Titan PD1A	Leyland H30/26R	Preston Corporation	88	RP
EED 8	1947	Leyland Titan PD1	Alexander H30/26R	Warrington Corporation	24	R
FFY 401	1947	Leyland Titan PD2/3	Leyland O30/26R	Southport Corporation	84	A
FFY 403	1947	Leyland Titan PD2/3	Leyland O30/26R	Southport Corporation	86	A
FFY 404	1947	Leyland Titan PD2/3	Leyland O30/26R	Southport Corporation	87	R
BCB 341	1948	Leyland Tiger PS1	Crossley B32F	Blackburn Corporation	8	A
DBU 246	1948	Leyland Titan PD1/3	Roe H31/25R	Oldham Corporation	246	R
KTD 768	1948	Leyland Titan PD2/1	Lydney L27/26R	Leigh Corporation	16	R
ACC 88	1949	Bedford OB	Duple C29F	Deiniolen Motors		A
FBU 827	1949	Crossley DD42/8	Crossley H30/26R	Oldham Corporation	368	A
ACB 902	1949	Guy Arab II	Northern Coach Builders H30/26R	Blackburn Corporation	74	A
CBV 431	1949	Guy Arab III	Crossley H30/26R	Blackburn Corporation	131	A
KTC 615	1949	Guy Arab III	Guy B33R	Accrington Corporation	10	A
BDJ 67	1950	AEC Regent III O961 RT	Park Royal H30/26R	St Helens Corporation	D67	R
EX 6644	1950	Crossley SD42/7	Yeates C35F	W J Haylett ('Felix Coaches'), Great Yarmouth		A
GFY 406	1950	Leyland Titan PD2/3	Leyland H30/26R	Southport Corporation	106	A
JND 629	1951	Leyland Titan PD2/3	Metro Cammell H32/26R	Manchester Corporation	3228	R
BDJ 808	1952	AEC Regent III O961 RT	Park Royal	St Helens Corporation	D8	A

Above: Seen in its home town of Warrington is Alexander-bodied Leyland PD1 No 24 built in 1947. *Philip Lamb*

Below: A later Warrington bus at St Helens is East Lancs-bodied Bristol RESL6G No 71 , also seen out and about, this time in the pleasant Cheshire village of Lymm. *Philip Lamb*

Registration	Date	Chassis	Body	New to	Fleet No	Status
NTF 466	1952	Daimler CVG5	Northern Counties B32F	Lancaster City Transport	466	R
RFM 644	1954	Guy Arab IV	Guy/Park Royal H30/26R	Chester Corporation	4	A
CDJ 878	1954	Leyland Titan PD2/9	Davies H30/26R	St Helens Corporation	E78	A
LDN 96	1955	AEC Regent III 6812A	Roe H33/27RD	York Pullman Bus Co	67	RP
ONE 744+	1956	BUT 9612T	Burlingham H33/26R	Manchester Corporation	1344	R
GDJ 435	1957	AEC Regent V MD3RV	Weymann H33/26R	St Helens Corporation	H135	A
434 BTE	1957	Crossley Regent V D3RV	East Lancashire Coachbuilders H31/28RD	Darwen Corporation	17	R
KRN 422	1957	Leyland Titan PD2/10	Crossley H33/29R	Preston Corporation	31	R
HDJ 753	1958	AEC Regent V D3RV	Weymann H33/26R	St Helens Corporation	J153	R
453 AUP	1958	AEC Reliance	Plaxton B45F	Wilkinson Bros, Sedgefield	53	R
GEN 201	1958	Leyland Titan PD3/6	Weymann H41/32RD	Bury Corporation	201	R
KDJ 999	1959	AEC Regent V 2D3RA	East Lancashire Coachbuilders H41/32F	St Helens Corporation	K199	A
FHF 456	1959	Leyland Atlantean PDR1/1	Metro Cammell H44/33F	Wallasey Corporation	6	A
PFR 346	1959	Leyland Titan PD2/27	Metro Cammell FH35/28RD	Blackpool Corporation	346	A
MSD 407	1959	Leyland Titan PD3/6	Alexander L35/32RD	Western SMT Co	AD1543	A
PBN 668	1960	Daimler CVG6-30	East Lancashire Coachbuilders H41/32F	Bolton Corporation	150	RP
LDJ 985	1960	Leyland Titan PD2A/27	Weymann H30/25RD	St Helens Corporation	K175	A
WLT 991	1961	AEC Routemaster R2RH	Park Royal H36/28R	London Transport	RM 991	R
562 RTF	1961	Leyland Titan PD2/40	East Lancashire Coachbuilders H37/28R	Widnes Corporation	31	R
TRJ 109	1962	AEC Reliance 2MU3RV	Weymann B45F	Salford City Transport	109	RP
152 CLT	1962	AEC Routemaster R2RH	Park Royal H36/28R	London Transport	RM 1152	R
574 TD	1962	Guy Arab IV	Northern Counties H41/32R	Lancashire United Transport	110	R
PSJ 480	1962	Leyland Titan PD2A/27	Massey H37/27F	Wigan Corporation	35	RP
OWJ 353A	1962	Leyland Titan PD3/4	Roe -	Doncaster Corporation	175	R
TDJ 612	1963	AEC Reliance 2MU3RA	Marshall B45F	St Helens Corporation	212	R
6219 TF	1963	Guy Arab IV	Northern Counties H41/32R	Lancashire United Transport	135	R
201 YTE	1963	Leyland Titan PD2/37	East Lancashire Coachbuilders O37/28F	Lancaster City Transport	201	R
8859 VR	1964	AEC Regent V 2D3RA	East Lancashire Neepsend H41/32F	'A Mayne & Son, Manchester'		R
AJA 139B	1964	Bedford VAL 14	Strachan B52F	North Western Road Car Co	139	RP
4227 FM	1964	Bristol Lodekka FS6G	ECW H33/27RD	Crosville Motor Services	DFG157	R
HTJ 521B	1964	Guy Arab V	Northern Counties H41/32F	Lancashire United Transport	165	RP
JTD 300B	1964	Guy Arab V	Northern Counties H41/32F	Lancashire United Transport	166	A
HTF 644B	1964	Leyland Titan PD2/40	East Lancashire Coachbuilders H37/28R	Widnes Corporation	38	R
FFM 135C	1965	Guy Arab V	Massey H41/32F	Chester Corporation	35	A
FFM 136C	1965	Guy Arab V	Massey H41/32F	Chester Corporation	36	R
BED 731C	1965	Leyland Titan PD2/40 Special	East Lancashire Coachbuilders H34/30F	Warrington Corporation	50	R
BCK 367C	1965	Leyland Titan PD3/6	Leyland/Preston Corporation H38/32F	Preston Corporation	61	A
CFR 590C	1965	Leyland Titan PD3A/1	Metro Cammell H41/30R	Blackpool Corporation	390	R
XTF 98D	1966	Leyland Titan PD3/4	East Lancashire Coachbuilders H41/32F	Haslington Corporation	45	A
MDJ 554E	1967	Leyland Titan PD2A/27	East Lancashire Coachbuilders H37/28R	St Helens Corporation	54	R
MDJ 555E	1967	Leyland Titan PD2A/27	East Lancashire Coachbuilders H37/28R	St Helens Corporation	55	A
FNC 304F	1968	Bedford VAS 5	Duffy/McArdle/MSs B33F	CIE School Bus	SS90	R
KJA 299G	1968	Bristol RESL6G	Marshall B43F	North Western Road Car Co	299	R
HCK 204G	1968	Leyland Panther PSUR1A/1R	MCW B47D	Preston Corporation	204	RP
LFR 529F	1968	Leyland Titan PD3/11	Metro Cammell H41/30R	Blackpool Corporation	529	RP
AFM 103G	1969	Bristol RELH6G	ECW C47F	Crosville Motor Services	CRG103	RP
AFM 106G	1969	Bristol RELH6G	ECW C47F	Crosville Motor Services	CRG106	A
JFM 650J	1969	Daimler Fleetline CRG6LX	Northern Counties H43/29F	Chester Corporation	50	RP

Registration	Date	Chassis	Body	New to	Fleet No	Status
DFM 347H	1969	Guy Arab V	Northern Counties H41/32F	Chester Corporation	47	A
SRJ 328H	1970	Leyland Atlantean PDR2/1	MCW H47/31D	SELNEC PTE	1205	A
JDJ 260K	1972	AEC Swift 3MP2R	Marshall B44D	St Helens Corporation	260	R
PDJ 269L	1972	AEC Swift 3MP2R	Marshall B42D	St Helens Corporation	269	RP
JMA 413L	1972	Bristol RELH6L	ECW C49F	North Western Road Car Co	413	R
DKC 305L	1972	Leyland Atlantean AN68/1R	Alexander H43/32F	Merseyside PTE	1305	RP
RTC 645L	1972	Leyland National 1151/1R/0101	Leyland National B52F	Widnes Corporation	1	R
LED 71P	1976	Bristol RESL6G	East Lancashire Coachbuilders B41D	Warrington Corporation	71	R
LTE 489P	1976	Leyland Leopard PSU3D/2R	Plaxton B48F	Lancashire United Transport	438	R
VBA 151S	1978	Leyland Atlantean AN68A/1R	Northern Counties H43/32F	Greater Manchester PTE	8151	R
ANA 551Y	1982	Leyland Atlantean AN68D/1R	Northern Counties H43/32F	Greater Manchester PTE	8551	RP

+ Trolleybus

Notes:

KJ 2578	Originally H24/24R; converted to canteen by Liverpool Corporation (CL4)
AFY 971	Originally H26/25R
RV 6360	Originally H26/24R; renumbered 6 following open-top conversion
DKY 713	Rebodied 1960
HLW 159	Acquired by Bradford City Transport (410) in 1958
FFY 403	Originally H30/26R
FFY 404	Originally H30/26R
FFY 401	Originally H30/26R
BDJ 808	Converted to breakdown vehicle by Harper Bros, Heath Hayes
PSJ 480	Originally registered JJP 502
OWJ 353A	Originally registered 475 HDT; converted to breakdown vehicle by South Yorkshire PTE and renumbered M3
201 YTE	Originally H37/28F
BCK 367C	Rebuilt from Leyland PD2 by Preston Corporation
FNC 304F	Originally registered EZL 90 in Irish Republic
DFM 347H	Last Guy Arab delivered to a British operator

Bury 201 from St Helens Transport Museum, but standing here at the Jericho terminus in its home town, is a Leyland PD3/6 with Weymann body, which entered service in 1958. *Philip Lamb*

Sandtoft Transport Centre

Contact address: Belton Road, Sandtoft, Doncaster DN8 5SX
Phone: 01724 711391
E-mail: enquiries@sandtoft.org.uk
Web site: www.sandtoft.org.uk
Brief description: Home of the nation's trolleybuses and the Sandtoft Miniature Railway
Events planned: 15/16 April 2001, 6/7 May 2001, 27/28 May 2001, 24 June 2001, 8 July 2001, Sandtoft Gathering Preview 28 July 2001, Sandtoft Gathering 29 July 2001, 12 August 2001, European Weekend 26/27 August 2001, Six-Wheeler Day 16 September 2001, Yorkshire Day 21 October 2001

Opening days/times: 12.00 to 17.00 on the above dates
Directions by car: From M180 junction 2, take A161 southbound to Belton. Turn right and museum is 2 miles on right-hand side.
Directions by public transport: Free bus from Doncaster station at 13.30 on 16 April, 7, 28 May, 24 June, 28/29 July, 27 August and 21 October (please telephone to check operation).
Charges: Adult £3.50, Child/Senior Citizen £2, Family £10. Other charges apply for gathering
Facilities: A B(e) D E F G H L P R S T
Other information: Coach tours and private party visits can be accommodated at other times by prior arrangement.

Registration	Date	Chassis	Body	New to	Fleet No	Status
1425 P+	1932	Fabrique Nationale	B26SD	Liege (Belgium)	425	RP
TV 9333+	1934	Karrier E6	Brush H64R	Nottingham City Transport	367	A
FW 8990+	1937	AEC 661T	Park Royal H30/26R	Cleethorpes Corporation	54	A
FTO 614	1939	AEC Regent O661		Nottingham City Transport	802	A
CET 613+	1942	Sunbeam MS2C	East Lancashire Coachbuilders B39C	Rotherham Corporation	74	A
964 H87+	1943	Vetra CB60	CTL B17D	Limoges (France)	5	R
GHN 574+	1944	Karrier W	East Lancashire Coachbuilders H39/31F	Bradford Corporation	792	R
GKP 511+	1944	Sunbeam W	Roe H34/28R	Maidstone Corporation	56	RP
CDT 636+	1945	Karrier W	Roe H34/28R	Doncaster Corporation	375	R
DKY 703+	1945	Karrier W	East Lancashire Coachbuilders H37/29F	Bradford Corporation	703	R
DKY 706+	1945	Karrier W	East Lancashire Coachbuilders H37/29F	Bradford Corporation	706	R
GTV 666+	1945	Karrier W	Brush UH30/26R	Nottingham City Transport	468	A
RC 8575+	1945	Sunbeam W	Park Royal UH30/26R	Derby Corporation	175	A
JV 9901	1947	AEC Regent III O961 RT	Roe H31/25R	Grimsby Corporation	81	RP
CVH 741+	1947	Sunbeam MS2	Park Royal H40/30R	Huddersfield Corporation	541	RP
HKR 11+	1947	Sunbeam W	Northern Coach Builders H30/26R	Maidstone Corporation	72	RP
JMN 727	1948	AEC Regent III O961	Northern Counties H30/26R	Douglas Corporation	63	R
KTV 493+	1948	BUT 9611T	Roe H31/25R	Nottingham City Transport	493	R
EKU 743+	1949	BUT 9611T	Roe H33/25R	Bradford Corporation	743	A
EKU 746+	1949	BUT 9611T	Roe H33/25R	Bradford Corporation	746	R
LHN 784+	1949	BUT 9611T	East Lancashire Coachbuilders H37/29F	Bradford Corporation	834	R
GDT 421	1949	Daimler CVD6	Roe L27/26R	Doncaster Corporation	112	A
BCK 939	1949	Leyland Titan PD1		Preston Corporation	6	R
EKY 558	1949	Leyland Titan PD2/3	Leyland H33/26R	Bradford Corporation	558	RP
GFU 692+	1950	BUT 9611T	Northern Coach Builders H38/26R	Cleethorpes Corporation	59	RP
KTV 506+	1950	BUT 9641T	Brush H38/32R	Nottingham City Transport	506	R
FET 617+	1950	Daimler CTE6	Roe H40/30R	Rotherham Corporation	37	RP
FET 618+	1950	Daimler CTE6	Roe H40/30R	Rotherham Corporation	44	A
GAJ 12+	1950	Sunbeam F4	Roe H35/26R	Tees-side Railless Traction Board	2	A
JWW 375+	1950	Sunbeam F4	East Lancashire Coachbuilders H37/29F	Bradford Corporation	845	A
JWW 376+	1950	Sunbeam F4	East Lancashire Coachbuilders H37/29F	Bradford Corporation	846	A
JWW 377+	1950	Sunbeam F4	East Lancashire Coachbuilders H37/29F	Bradford Corporation	847	A
ERD 152+	1950	Sunbeam S7	Park Royal H38/30RD	Reading Corporation	181	R
KDT 393	1951	AEC Regal III 9613A	Roe H31/25R	Doncaster Corporation	122	A

Registration	Date	Chassis	Body	New to	Fleet No	Status
BDJ 87+	1951	BUT 9611T	East Lancashire Coachbuilders H30/26R	St Helens Corporation	387	A
FKU 758+	1951	BUT 9611T	Weymann H33/26R	Bradford Corporation	758	A
MDT 222	1953	AEC Regal III 9621A	Roe B39F	Doncaster Corporation	22	R
OTV 137	1953	AEC Regent III 9613E	Park Royal H30/26R	Nottingham City Transport	137	RP
JDN 668	1954	AEC Regent III 6812A	Roe H33/25RD	York Pullman Bus Co	64	R
TDH 914+	1955	Sunbeam F4A	Willowbrook H36/34RD	Walsall Corporation	864	A
KVH 219+	1956	BUT 9641T	East Lancashire Coachbuilders H40/32R	Huddersfield Corporation	619	A
XWX 795	1959	AEC Reliance 2MU3RV	Roe C—F	Felix Motors, Doncaster	40	A
9629 WU	1960	AEC Reliance 2MU3RV	Roe DP41F	Felix Motors, Doncaster	41	R
KSK 270+	1960	Schindler SWR Chassisless	Schindler B27T	Lucerne (Switzerland)	227	R
VRD 193+	1961	Sunbeam F4A	Burlingham H38/30F	Reading Corporation	193	R
657 BWB	1962	Leyland Atlantean PDR1/1	Park Royal H44/33F	Sheffield Joint Omnibus Committee	1357	R
KHC 369	1963	AEC Regent V 2D3RV	East Lancashire Coachbuilders H32/28RD	Eastbourne Corporation	69	R
433 MDT	1963	Leyland Tiger Cub PSUC1/11	Roe B45F	Doncaster Corporation	33	R
JTF 920B	1964	AEC Reliance 2MU3RV	East Lancashire Coachbuilders B—D	Reading Corporation	48	A
KDT 206D	1966	Daimler CVG6LX	Roe H34/28F	Doncaster Corporation	206	RP
66+	1967	Lancia	Dalfa H43/25D	Oporto (Portugal)	140	R
UDT 455F	1968	Leyland Royal Tiger Cub RTC1/2	Roe B45D	Doncaster Corporation	55	R
WWJ 754M	1973	Daimler Fleetline CRG6LXB	Park Royal H43/27D	Sheffield Transport	754	R
ERU 159V	1979	Leyland Fleetline FE30ALR	Alexander H43/31F	Bournemouth Transport	159	R
C45 HDT+	1985	Dennis Dominator DTA1401	Alexander H47/33F	South Yorkshire PTE	2450	R
+ Trolleybus						

Notes:

FTO 614	Converted to tower wagon.	GAJ 12	Rebodied 1964
964 H87	French registration.	JWW 375	Rebodied 1962; chassis ex-Mexborough & Swinton
GHN 574	Originally single-decker; rebodied 1958	JWW 376	Rebodied 1962; chassis ex-Mexborough & Swinton
GKP 511	Rebodied 1960	JWW 377	Rebodied 1962; chassis ex-Mexborough & Swinton
CDT 636	Rebodied 1955	KSK 270	Registration not carried
DKY 703	Rebodied 1960	657 BWB	Rebodied 1968; renumbered 227 in 1970 following
DKY 706	Rebodied 1960		dissolution of JOC
HKR 11	On loan from Maidstone Borough Council	JTF 920B	Caravan conversion; originally registered 5148 DP
LHN 784	Rebodied 1962; chassis new to Darlington	66	Portuguese registration.
BCK 939	Converted to breakdown vehicle	C45 HDT	Experimental vehicle; originally registered B450 CKW.
FET 618	Rebodied 1956 (formerly single-decker)		

Sandtoft Transport Centre is home to a number of groups including the Felix Transport Group, which maintains two AEC Reliances there. Seen here is Roe dual-purpose-bodied No 41, dating from 1960. *Tony Wilson*

Contact address: M90 Commerce Park, Lathalmond, Fife, KY12 OSY
Phone: 01383 623380
E-mail: website: www.busweb.co.uk/svbm
Affiliation: NARTM
Brief description: The collection of over 160 buses was, in the main, operated or manufactured in Scotland, from the late 1920s to the early 1980s. Vehicles are generally owned by private individuals or groups. A fully-equipped workshop enables comprehensive restoration to be undertaken. The 42-acre site is a former Royal Navy depot.

Events planned: 18/19 August 2001 — open weekend.
Opening days/times: Easter to end of September, Sundays 13.00 to 17.00.
Directions by car: Use M90 junction 3. Take B914 Dollar road. Left B915 Dunfermline (2 miles). 2 miles to M90 Commerce Park on right.
Directions by public transport: Nearest bus/train Dunfermline. No public transport to site.
Charges: Sunday opening £2. Other charges apply for open weekend.
Facilities: B B(e) D E P R S T

Registration	Date	Chassis	Body	New to	Fleet No	Status
GE 2446	1928	Leyland Titan TD1	Leyland L27/24RO	Glasgow Corporation	111	R
RU 8678	1929	Leyland Lion PLSC3	Leyland B35F	Hants & Dorset Motor Services	268	A
SO 3740	1929	Leyland Tiger TS2	Alexander B32F	Scottish General (Northern) Omnibus Co	P63	R
note o	1934	Body only	Cowieson B—R	Scottish Motor Traction Co	B124	A
VD 3433	1934	Leyland Lion LT5A	Alexander B36F	W Alexander & Sons	P721	R
AAA 756	1935	Albion Victor PK114	Abbott C20C	King Alfred Motor Services		R
WG 3260	1935	Leyland Lion LT5A	Alexander B35F	W Alexander & Sons	P705	A
ATF 477	1937	Leyland Tiger TS7T	Fowler B39F	Singleton of Leyland		A
WG 8107	1939	Leyland Tiger TS8	Alexander	W Alexander & Sons	P528	R
WG 8790	1939	Leyland Tiger TS8	Alexander B39F	W Alexander & Sons	P573	A
AUX 296	1939	Sentinel-HSG	Cowieson B32R	Sentinel, Shrewsbury - demonstrator		A
ETJ 108	1940	Leyland Tiger TS11	Roe	Leigh Corporation	79	RP
HF 9126	1940	Leyland Titan TD7	Metro Cammell	Wallasey Corporation	74	A
DSG 169	1942	Leyland Titan TD5	Alexander L27/26R	Scottish Motor Traction Co	J66	R
CDR 679	1943	Guy Arab II	Roe	Plymouth Corporation	249	RP
JWS 594	1943	Guy Arab II	Duple/Nudd H31/24R	London Transport	G 77	R
VV 9135	1944	Daimler CWD6	Duple H30/26R	Northampton Corporation	135	A
BRS 37	1945	Daimler CWD6	Duple H30/26R	Aberdeen Corporation	155	RP
AWG 639	1946	AEC Regal I 0662	Alexander C35F	W Alexander & Sons	A52	R
AWG 623	1947	AEC Regal I 0662	Alexander C30F	W Alexander & Sons	A36	R
XG 9304	1947	Leyland Titan PD1A	Northern Counties L27/26R	Middlesborough Corporation	52	A
BWG 39	1948	Bedford OB	Scottish Motor Traction C25F	W Alexander & Sons	W218	RP
BMS 405	1948	Daimler CVD6	Burlingham C33F	W Alexander & Sons	D10	RP
GGA 670	1948	Foden PVS6G	Plaxton C35F	SCWS, Glasgow		RP
AWG 393	1948	Guy Arab III	Cravens H30/26R	W Alexander & Sons	RO607	R
ESG 652	1948	Guy Arab III	Metro Cammell B35R	Edinburgh Corporation	739	R
KTF 589	1949	AEC Regent III 9612E	Park Royal O33/26R	Morecambe & Heysham Corporation	60	R
FSC 182	1949	Daimler CVG6	Metro Cammell H31/25R	Edinburgh Corporation	135	R
SJ 1340	1950	Bedford OB	Duple C29F	Lennox, Brodick		A
SS 7486	1950	Bedford OB	Duple C29F	Stark's Motor Services, Dunbar		A
SS 7501	1950	Bedford OB	Duple C29F	Fairbairn, Haddington		R
DCS 616	1950	Daimler CVD6	Massey O32/28RD	Hunter (A1), Dreghorn	16A	R
EVA 324	1950	Guy Arab III	Guy B33R	Central SMT Co	K24	R
GVD 47	1950	Guy Arab III	Duple H31/26R	Hutchinson's Coaches, Overtown		RP
DMS 820	1950	Leyland Tiger OPS2/1	Alexander C35F	W Alexander & Sons	PB7	A
CWG 283	1950	Leyland Tiger PS1	Alexander C35F	W Alexander & Sons	PA181	RP
MTE 639	1951	AEC Regent III 6812A	Weymann H33/26R	Morecambe & Heysham Corporation	77	R
DMS 823	1951	Leyland Tiger OPS2/1	Alexander C35F	W Alexander & Sons	PB10	RP
DGS 536	1951	Leyland Tiger PS1/1	McLennan C39F	A & C McLennan, Spittalfield		R

A long way from its home city is King Alfred AAA 756. The duties of this 1935 Abbott-bodied Albion Victor included acting as personal conveyance to its owners, the Chisnell family. Owned by well-known preservationist Dave Hurley, the Victor is currently a Lathalmond resident. *Tony Wilson*

Registration	Date	Chassis	Body	New to	Fleet No	Status
DGS 625	1951	Leyland Tiger PS1/1	McLennan C39F	A & C McLennan, Spittalfield		R
BMS 222	1952	Leyland Royal Tiger PSU1/15	Alexander C41C	W Alexander & Sons	PC1	R
CYJ 252	1953	AEC Regent III 9613E	Alexander H32/26R	Dundee Corporation	137	R
NXP 506	1953	Bedford SB	Plaxton C33F	D Halley, Sauchie		R
GM 6384	1954	Leyland Titan PD2/10	Leyland L27/28R	Central SMT Co	L484	A
LFS 480	1954	Leyland Titan PD2/20	Metro Cammell H34/29R	Edinburgh Corporation	480	R
TYD 888	1955	AEC Reliance MU3RV	Duple C43F	Wakes, Sparkford		R
FWG 846	1955	Bristol LS6G	ECW B45F	W Alexander & Sons	E11	A
OWS 620	1957	Bristol Lodekka LD6G	ECW H33/27R	Scottish Omnibuses	AA620	RP
OFS 777	1957	Leyland Titan PD2/20	Metro Cammell H34/29R	Edinburgh Corporation	777	R
OFS 798	1957	Leyland Titan PD2/20	Metro Cammell H34/29R	Edinburgh Corporation	798	RP
SWS 671	1959	AEC Reliance 2MU3RV	Alexander C38F	Scottish Omnibuses	B671	R
SWS 715	1959	AEC Reliance 2MU3RV	Park Royal C41F	Scottish Omnibuses	715	A
J 1359	1959	Albion Victor FT39KAN	Reading B35F	Jersey Motor Transport Co	5	RP
1252 EV	1959	Bristol MW5G	ECW DP41F	Eastern National Omnibus Co	488	R
EDS 320A	1960	AEC Routemaster R2RH	Park Royal H36/28R	London Transport	RM 606	A
EDS 50A	1960	AEC Routemaster R2RH	Park Royal H36/28R	London Transport	RM 560	R
WAJ 112	1960	Albion Nimbus NS3N	Plaxton C29F	Watson, Huntingdon		A
XLS 945A	1960	Bristol MW6G	Alexander C41F	Western SMT Co	T1590	A
XSN 25A	1960	Bristol MW6G	Alexander C41F	Western SMT Co	T1591	A
RAG 578	1960	Daimler CVG6LX	Northern Counties FH41/32F	J Hunter (A1), Kilmarnock		RP
VSC 86	1960	Leyland Tiger Cub PSUC1/3	Weymann B47F	Edinburgh Corporation	86	R
EDS 288A	1961	AEC Routemaster R2RH	Park Royal H36/28R	London Transport	RM 910	R
RAG 411	1961	Bristol Lodekka LD6G	ECW H33/27RD	Western SMT Co	1645	R
UCX 275	1961	Guy Wulfrunian	Roe H43/32F	County Motors, Lepton	99	R

Registration	Date	Chassis	Body	New to	Fleet No	Status
YSG 101	1961	Leyland Leopard PSU3/2R	Alexander B33T	Edinburgh Corporation	101	R
YYJ 914	1961	Leyland Tiger Cub PSUC1/2	Alexander C41F	Stark's Motor Services, Dunbar	H8	A
RCS 382	1961	Leyland Titan PD3A/3	Alexander L35/32RD	Western SMT Co	1684	R
7424 SP	1962	AEC Reliance 2MU3RV	Alexander C41F	W Alexander & Sons (Fife) Ltd	FAC4	R
NSJ 502	1962	AEC Reliance 2MU3RV	Alexander C41F	W Alexander & Sons (Northern)	NAC205	RP
LDS 201A	1962	AEC Routemaster	Park Royal H36/28R	London Transport	RM 1607	R
UCS 659	1963	Albion Lowlander LR3	Northern Counties H40/31F	Western SMT Co	N1795	R
ARG 17B	1964	AEC Reliance 2MU3RA	Alexander C41F	W Alexander & Sons (Northern) Ltd	NAC246	RP
AFS 91B	1964	AEC Reliance 4MU3RA	Alexander B53F	Eastern Scottish	B91	R
AWA 124B	1964	Bedford SB13	Duple C41F	J O Andrew, Sheffield		R
BXA452B	1964	Bristol Lodekka FS6G	ECW H33/27RD	W Alexander & Sons (Fife) Ltd	FAC4	R
BXA 464B	1964	Bristol Lodekka FS6G	ECW H33/27RD	W Alexander & Sons (Fife) Ltd	FRD199	RP
ASC 665B	1964	Leyland Titan PD3/6	Alexander H41/29F	Edinburgh Corporation	665	R
ESF 801C	1965	Leyland Atlantean PDR1/1	Alexander H43/31F	Edinburgh Corporation	801	R
FFV 447D	1966	AEC Reliance 2U3RA	Plaxton C45F	J Abbott & Sons, Blackpool		RP
KBD 714D	1966	Bristol Lodekka FS6G	ECW H33/27RD	United Counties Omnibus Co	714	A
EWS 168D	1966	Bristol RELH6G	Alexander C38Ft	Scottish Omnibuses	XA168	A
WTE 155D	1966	Guy Arab V	Northern Counties H41/30F	Lancashire United Transport	232	RP
LUS 524E	1967	AEC Reliance 2U3RA	Willowbrook C49F	David MacBrayne, Glasgow	150	R
NMY 634E	1967	AEC Routemaster R2RH/2	Park Royal H32/24F	British European Airways	8241	R
GRS 343E	1967	Albion Viking VK43AL	Alexander DP40F	W Alexander & Sons (Northern) Ltd	NNV43	R
HGM 335E	1967	Bristol Lodekka FLF6G	ECW H44/34F	Central SMT Co	BL335	R
HGM 346E	1967	Bristol Lodekka FLF6G	ECW H44/34F	Central SMT Co	BL346	R
KPM 91E	1967	Bristol Lodekka FLF6G	ECW O32/28F	Brighton Hove & District Omnibus Co	91	R
HDV 639E	1967	Bristol MW6G	ECW C39F	Western National Omnibus Co	1434	R
JSC 900E	1967	Leyland Atlantean PDR2/1	Alexander O47/35F	Edinburgh Corporation	900	R
NTY 416F	1968	AEC Reliance 6MU3R	Plaxton C45F	J Rowell, Prudhoe		RP
VMP 8G	1968	Albion Viking VK43AL	Alexander DP40F	Road Transport Industry Training Board	16	A
KGM 664F	1968	Leyland Leopard PSU3/1R	Alexander B53F	Central SMT Co	T64	A
VMP 10G	1969	AEC Reliance 6U3ZR	Alexander B57F	Road Transport Industry Training Board	24	R
NAG 120G	1969	Bristol REMH6G	Alexander C42Ft	Western SMT Co	T2214	RP
XFM 42G	1969	Guy Arab V	Northern Counties H41/32F	Chester Corporation	42	R
TMS 585H	1970	Leyland Leopard PSU3/1R	Alexander C49F	Road Transport Industry Training Board	84	RP
VFU 864J	1971	Bedford J2	Plaxton C—F	Hardings, Lincolnshire		A
TGM 214J	1971	Daimler Fleetline CRG6LX	ECW H43/34F	Central SMT Co	D14	RP
SXA 63K	1971	Daimler Fleetline CRG6LXB	Alexander H44/31F	W Alexander & Sons (Fife)	FRF63	A
AMS 513K	1971	Leyland Leopard PSU3/3R	Alexander	W Alexander & Sons (Midland) Ltd	MPE113	R
BFS 1L	1972	Leyland Atlantean AN68/1R	Alexander H45/30D	Edinburgh Corporation	1	R
BWG 833L	1972	Leyland Leopard PSU3/3R	Alexander B53F	W Alexander & Sons (Midland) Ltd	MPE133	A
YSD 350L	1972	Leyland Leopard PSU3/3R	Alexander B41F	Western SMT Co	L2390	R
BFS 463L	1973	Bedford YRQ	Alexander DP45F	Scottish Omnibuses ('Eastern Scottish')	C463	A
BWS 105L	1973	Seddon Pennine VII-236	Seddon DP25F	Edinburgh Corporation	105	R
SCS 333M	1974	Leyland Leopard PSU3/3R	Alexander B53F	Western SMT Co	L2464	RP
SCS 366M	1974	Leyland Leopard PSU3/3R	Alexander B53F	Western SMT Co	L2497	RP
IIL 4595	1976	Bedford YRQ	Plaxton C45F	Reid & Mackay, Edinburgh		R
NCS 16P	1976	Leyland Fleetline FE30AGR	Alexander H43/31F	Hill (A1), Stevenston		RP
MSF 750P	1976	Seddon Pennine VII	Alexander C42Ft	Scottish Omnibuses ('Eastern Scottish')	XS750	R
SSC 212P	1976	Volvo Ailsa AB57	Alexander H—F	Tayside Regional Council	107	RP
SMS 120P	1977	Daimler Fleetline CRG6LXB	Alexander H44/31F	W Alexander & Sons (Midland) Ltd	MRF120	RP
OSJ 629R	1977	Leyland Leopard PSU3C/3R	Alexander B53F	Western SMT Co	L2629	RP
XMS 252R	1977	Leyland Leopard PSU3C/4R	Alexander B53F	W Alexander & Sons (Midland) Ltd	MPE252	A
RRS 46R	1977	Leyland Leopard PSU3E/4R	Duple C49F	W Alexander & Sons (Northern) Ltd	NPE46	R
ORS 60R	1977	Leyland Leopard PSU4C/4F	Alexander C45F	Grampian	60	R
NDL 656R	1978	Bristol VRTSL3/6LXB	ECW H43/31F	Southern Vectis Omnibus Co	656	RP

Above: Seen inside the display hall at Lathalmond is Alexander A52, a 1947 AEC Regal, bodied by its operator. *Philip Lamb*

Below: The Alexander 'Y'-type body has been a familiar sight in Scotland for more than three decades. It is seen here fitted to AEC Reliance VMP 10G, new to the Road Transport Industry Training Board as its No 24, but presented at Lathalmond as a vehicle in the well-known Baxters of Airdrie fleet. *Philip Lamb*

Registration	Date	Chassis	Body	New to	Fleet No	Status
CSG 792S	1978	Seddon Pennine VII	Plaxton C45F	Scottish Omnibuses ('Eastern Scottish')	S792	RP
JSF 928T	1978	Seddon Pennine VII	Alexander DP49F	Scottish Omnibuses	S928	RP
LSC 936T	1978	Seddon Pennine VII	Alexander DP49F	Scottish Omnibuses ('Eastern Scottish')	S936	A
CSG 773S	1978	Volvo Ailsa B55-10	Alexander H43/32F	Scottish Omnibuses ('Eastern Scottish')	VV773	A
LIL 9929	1979	Bedford PJK	Plaxton C29F	Blood Transfusion Service		RP
JSX 595T	1979	Leyland Atlantean AN68A/1R	Alexander H45/30D	Lothian Regional Transport	595	R
DSD 936V	1979	Seddon Pennine VII	Alexander C49F	Western SMT Co	S2936	A
SSX 602V	1979	Seddon Pennine VII	Alexander B53F	Scottish Omnibuses ('Eastern Scottish')	S602	RP
ESF 647W	1980	Guy Victory Mk 2	Alexander H60/24D	China Motor Bus	LV36	R
HSC 173X	1980	Leyland Cub	Duple B31F	Lothian Regional Transport	173	RP
VSF 542V	1980	Leyland Fleetline FE30AGR	Alexander H56/36D	China Motor Bus	SF31	R
RHS 400W	1980	Wales & Edwards	Wales & Edwards B12F	South of Scotland Electricity		R
GSC 658X	1981	Leyland Atlantean AN68A/1R	Alexander H45/30D	Lothian Regional Transport	658	A
FES 831W	1981	Volvo B58-61	Duple B59F	Stagecoach, Perth		A
NFS 176Y	1982	Leyland Leopard PSU3G/4R	Alexander C49F	Alexander (Fife)	FPE176	RP
ULS 716X	1982	Leyland Leopard PSU3G/4R	Alexander C49F	Alexander (Midland)	MPE416	RP
ULS 717X	1982	Leyland Leopard PSU3G/4R	Alexander C49F	Alexander (Midland)	MPE417	RP
GSC 667X	1982	Leyland Olympian ONTL11/1R	Alexander H47/28D	Lothian Regional transport	667	R

Notes:

SO 3740 — Passed to W Alexander & Sons in 1930; numbered P63 in 1932 and rebodied in 1934

VD 3433 — Rebodied 1945

WG 8107 — Breakdown Vehicle. Originally C35F.

ETJ 108 — Breakdown Vehicle

HF 9126 — Originally H28/26R; acquired by Lancaster County Constabulary in 1952 and converted for use as mobile control post

DSG 169 — Alexander body to Leyland design; converted to open-top in 1959 and restored in 1980/1

CDR 679 — Converted to platform lorry for farm use in 1963

JWS 594 — Originally London Transport G77 (GLL577); rebuilt and rebodied 1953

KTF 589 — Originally H33/26R

SS 7486 — Passed to Scottish Omnibuses (C22) in 1964

DCS 616 — Rebodied in 1958 as H32/28RD

GVD 47 — Acquired by McGill's Bus Services, Barrhead, in 1952

EDS 50A — Originally registered WLT 560; acquired by Stagecoach, Perth, in 1985

EDS 320A — Originally registered WLT 606; acquired by Kelvin Scottish Omnibuses (1919) in 1986

XLS 945A — Originally registered OCS 712

XSN 25A — Originally registered OCS 713

EDS 288A — Originally registered WLT 910; acquired by Kelvin Scottish Omnibuses (1929) in 1986

UCX 275 — On loan from Dewsbury Bus Museum

YYJ 914 — Originally registered ESS 989

LDS 201A — Originally registered 607 DYE; acquired by Stagecoach, Perth, in 1986

NMY 634E — Passed to London Transport (RMA50) in 1979; acquired by Stagecoach, Perth, in 1987

KPM 91E — Originally H38/32F; acquired by Scottish Omnibuses (AA971) in 1973 and converted to open-top (as OT2) in 1983

HDV 639E — First vehicle operated by Stagecoach

JSC 900E — Originally H47/35F

AMS 513K — Originally C49F; converted to breakdown vehicle

YSD 350L — Originally C49F; rebuilt and shortened by Western SMT in 1980

SSC 212P — Display vehicle; originally registered LES 44P

NDL 656R — Acquired by Lowland Scottish Omnibuses (856) in 1991

LIL 9929 — Original identity unknown

ESF 647W — Original Hong Kong registration was CH 9399

RHS 400W — Battery-electric bus

FES 831W — First new vehicle delivered to Stagecoach (as C50Ft)

Top right: Normally at Lathalmond, but seen here in Halifax is this unique three-door Leyland Leopard. Bodied by Alexander, Edinburgh 101 entered service in 1961. *Tony Wilson*

Right: Craven-bodied Guy Arab III Alexander RO607 was built in 1948, and has been in the care of a preservationist longer than it was in service. *Philip Lamb*

Contact address: Tinsley Tram Sheds, Sheffield Road, Tinsley, Sheffield S9 2FY
Phone: 0114 255 3010
E-mail: website:
http://freespace.virgin.net/neil.worthington/sheff/page1~1.htm
Brief description: The display of over 20 vehicles is housed in part of a former tram shed.
Events planned:
15 April 2001, 10 June 2001, 12 August 2001 — open days;
19 September 2001 — Meadowhall Rally;

14 October 2001, 9 December 2001 — open days.
Opening days/times: Open days as above; also most Saturdays and Sundays (not Christmas) 12.00 to 16.00 (please telephone to check opening times before travelling).
Directions by car: From M1 Junction 34 take A6178.
Directions by public transport: By Supertram to Carbrook (200yd from museum); also good bus links from Sheffield and Rotherham.
Charges: Adult £1, concession 50p, Family £2.
Facilities: B(e)

Registration	Date	Chassis	Body	New to	Fleet No	Status
WG 9180	1940	Leyland Titan TD7	Leyland L27/26R	W Alexander & Sons	P266	R
GWJ 724	1941	AEC Regent O661	Sheffield Transport Department	Sheffield Corporation	G54	A
JWB 416	1947	Leyland Tiger PS1	Weymann B34R	Sheffield Corporation	216	A
KWE 255	1948	AEC Regent III 9612E	MCW	Sheffield Corporation	G55	A
HD 7905	1948	Leyland Tiger PS1	Brush B34F	Yorkshire Woollen District Transport Co	622	RP
MHY 765	1950	Leyland Comet ECPO/1R	Duple C32F	Orient Coaches, Bristol		RP
ACW 645	1950	Leyland Titan PD2/1	Leyland H30/26R	Burnley Colne & Nelson Joint Committee	63	R
OWE 116	1952	AEC Regent III 9613A	Roe H33/25R	Sheffield Joint Omnibus Committee	116	A
KET 220	1954	Daimler CVG6	Weymann H30/26R	Rotherham Corporation	220	RP
RWB 87	1954	Leyland Titan PD2/12	Weymann H32/26R	Sheffield Corporation	687	RP
WRA 12	1955	AEC Monocoach MC3RV	Park Royal B45F	Booth & Fisher, Halfway		R
VDV 760	1958	Bristol Lodekka LD6G	ECW H33/27RD	Western National Omnibus Co	1943	A
PFN 858	1959	AEC Regent V 2LD3RA	Park Royal FH40/32F	East Kent Road Car Co		A
TDK 322	1959	AEC Regent V D2RA	Weymann H33/28RD	Rochdale Corporation	322	R
TET 135	1959	Daimler CVG6-30	Roe	Rotherham Corporation		R
6330 WJ	1960	AEC Regent V 2D3RA	Roe H39/30RD	Sheffield Joint Omnibus Committee	1330	A
7874 WJ	1960	AEC Regent V 2D3RA	Alexander H37/32R	Sheffield Corporation	874	R
1322 WA	1961	AEC Reliance 2MU3RA	Plaxton C36F	Sheffield United Tours	322	A
NAT 766A	1962	Daimler CVG6-30	Roe H39/31F	Grimsby - Cleethorpes Transport	57	RP
GHD 765	1962	Leyland Titan PD3A/1	Metro Cammell H39/31F	Yorkshire Woollen District Transport Co	893	R
DWB 54H	1970	AEC Swift 5P2R	Park Royal B50F	Sheffield Transport	54	RP
AHA 451J	1971	Leyland Leopard PSU4B/4R	Plaxton C40F	BMMO ('Midland Red')	6451	R
MGE 183P	1975	Ailsa B55-10	Van Hool McArdle H44/35F	Glasgow Corporation	AV8	A
LWB 383P	1976	Volvo Ailsa B55-10	Van Hool McArdle H44/31D	South Yorkshire PTE	383	R
LWB 388P	1976	Volvo Ailsa B55-10	Van Hool McArdle H44/31D	South Yorkshire PTE	388	RP
PSJ 825R	1976	Volvo Ailsa B55-10	Van Hool McArdle H44/31F	J Hunter (A1), Kilmarnock		R
OKW 515R	1977	Daimler Fleetline FE30AGR	MCW H—F	South Yorkshire PTE	1515	A

Notes:

GWJ 724	Originally bus 462; converted to grit wagon		NAT 766A	Originally registered TJV 100.
KWE 255	Originally bus 255; converted to grit wagon		PSJ 825R	Ofiginally H44/31D
TET 135	Originally H39/31F; converted to breakdown vehicle			

Yorkshire Woollen 893, a 1963 Metro-Cammell-bodied Leyland PD3A/1, can today be found at the Sheffield Bus Museum. *Philip Lamb*

Tameside Transport Collection Mossley

Contact address: Roaches Industrial Estate, Manchester Road, Mossley, Greater Manchester

Brief description: A working museum comprising a small but varied collection of vehicles ranging from 1929 to the 1960s. There is in addition a display of transport-related items.

Opening days/times: Last weekend of each month, 10.00 to 15.00; visits at other times by prior appointment.

Directions by car:

From Ashton-under-Lyne take A635 (Huddersfield) through Mossley. Museum is 1 mile on right-hand side, adjacent to Shadows Lane.

Directions by public transport:
Bus service 355 from Ashton-under-Lyne or Oldham.
By rail to Mossley station (approximately 1 mile walk).

Charges: No charge but donations welcome.

Facilities: D S R T

Other information: Car parking is limited.

Registration	Date	Chassis	Body	New to	Fleet No	Status
LG 2637	1929	Crossley Arrow	Crossley B32R	S Jackson & Sons, Crewe		A
DNF 204	1937	Crossley Mancunian	Metro Cammell/Crossley B32R	Manchester Corporation	129	RP
HG 9651	1948	Leyland Tiger PS1	Brush B35R	Burnley Colne & Nelson Joint Committee	10	R
DBN 978	1949	Crossley SD42/7	Crossley B32R	Bolton Corporation	8	R
JND 728	1950	Daimler CVG6	Metro Cammell H32/26R	Manchester Corporation	4127	R
CRC 911	1951	Crossley DD42/8A	Brush H30/26R	Derby Corporation	111	R
FRJ 511	1951	Daimler CVG6	Metro Cammell H30/24R	Salford City Transport	511	R
422 CAX	1961	AEC Regent V MD3RV	Massey L31/28R	Bedwas & Machen UDC	5	R
7209 PW	1962	Bedford J2SZ2	Plaxton C20F	H & I Jarvis, Downham Market		R
105 UTU	1962	Leyland Titan PD2/37	Northern Counties H36/28F	SHMD Board	5	RP
BWO 585B	1964	AEC Regent V 2MD3RA	Massey L31/28R	Bedwas & Machen UDC	8	R
NMA 328D	1966	Daimler Fleetline CRG6LX	Northern Counties H43/31F	SHMD Board	28	RP

Notes:
LG 2637   Passed to Crosville Motor Services (U2) in 1934

Transport Museum Society of Ireland Howth

Contact address: Howth Castle Demesne, Howth, Dublin 13, Ireland

Phone: (00) 353 1 832 0427

Affiliation: NARTM

Brief description: The museum is run by a group of volunteers dedicated to the preservation and restoration of valuable road transport heritage. Exhibits include buses, trams and commercial, public utility, military, fire-appliance, electric and horse-drawn vehicles. Other displays include transport-associated memorabilia. The museum is a registered charity.

Opening days/times: June to August: Monday to Saturday 10.00 to 17.00; Sunday 14.00 to 17.00.

September to May: Saturdays, Sundays and Bank Holidays 14.00 to 17.00.

Directions by car: Howth is 9 miles north of Dublin City Centre or 7 miles from the M1/M50 junction at Dublin Airport. Museum is located in grounds of Howth Castle Demesne.

Directions by public transport: Bus 31 from Dublin City Centre; Local DART rail service to Howth station, then short walk.

Charges: Adult £1.60, Child 80p, Family £4 (group discounts available).

Facilities: E G P T

Other information: Limited access for disabled.

Registration	Date	Chassis	Body	New to	Fleet No	Status
TE 5110	1928	Leyland Lion PLSC3	(chassis only)	Colne Corporation	22	A
note i	1933	AEC Regal I	(chassis only)	(unknown)		A
ZI 9708	1933	Dennis Lancet I	Dublin United Tramways Co B32R	Dublin United Tramways Co	F21	A
ZC 714	1937	Leyland Titan TD4	Leyland H32/26R	Dublin United Tramways Co	R1	R
FRU 305	1945	Bristol K6A	Hants & Dorset FO31/28R	Hants & Dorset Motor Services	1108	A
GZ 7638	1947	Leyland Tiger PS1	Northern Ireland Road Transport Bd B34R	Northern Ireland Road Transport Board	A8560	A

Registration	Date	Chassis	Body	New to	Fleet No	Status
ZH 3926	1948	AEC Regal III O962	Park Royal C35R	Great Northern Railway (Ireland)	427	A
ZH 3937	1948	AEC Regent III 9612E	Park Royal H30/26RD	Great Northern Railway (Ireland)	438	R
IY 1940	1948	AEC Regent III 9621E	Park Royal O33/26R	Morecambe & Heysham Corporation	58	A
ZD 7163	1948	Leyland Tiger OPS3	(chassis only)	CIE	P23	A
ZH 4538	1948	Leyland Titan PD2/3	Leyland H33/27R	CIE	R389	R
LTU 869	1949	Commer Avenger I	Plaxton C33F	Thornley, Woodley		A
ZL 2718	1950	GNR Gardner	PRV-GNR	Great Northern Railway (Ireland)	387	A
MZ 7396	1950	Guy Arab III	Harkness B31F	Belfast Corporation	298	A
GUX 188	1951	Bedford OB	Duple B31F	Lloyd, Oswestry		A
IY 7384	1951	GNR Gardner	PRV-GNR DP33R	Great Northern Railway (Ireland)	390	RP
ZJ 5933	1951	Leyland Tiger OPS3	CIE	CIE	P193	A
OZ 6686	1953	Daimler CVG6	Harkness H30/26R	Belfast Corporation	432	A
ZO 6819	1953	Leyland Tiger PS2/14	CIE B39R	CIE	P309	A
ZO 6857	1953	Leyland Tiger PS2/14	CIE B39R	CIE	P347	R
ZL 6816	1953	Leyland Titan OPD2/1	CIE H37/31R	CIE	R506	A
ZY 79	1954	AEC Regal IV 9822E	PRV-GNR B45R	Great Northern Railway (Ireland)	274	A
ZO 6881	1954	Leyland Royal Tiger PSU1/15	CIE C34C	CIE	U10	A
ZO 6949	1954	Leyland Royal Tiger PSU1/15	CIE B39D	CIE	U78	A
ZU 9241	1955	Leyland Titan OPD2/1	CIE H37/31RD	CIE	R567	A
CYI 621	1958	Leyland Titan PD2 OPD2/2	CIE	CIE	R819	A
UI 8511	1960	Leyland Tiger Cub	Dundalk B45	Londonderry & Lough Swilly Railway Co	83	A
HZA 230	1960	Leyland Titan PD3/2	CIE H41/33R	CIE	RA105	RP
HZA 279	1961	AEC Regent V 2D2RA	CIE H41/28RD	CIE	AA2	A
404 RIU	1963	Albion Lowlander	Alexander H41/31F	W Alexander & Sons (Midland) Ltd	MRE38	A
HZD 593	1963	Leyland Worldmaster ERT2/1	Van Hool DP53F	CIE	WVH13	A
NZE 598	1964	Leyland Leopard L2	CIE B45F	CIE	E170	A
NZE 620	1964	Leyland Titan PD3A/6	Dundalk (Park Royal frame) H41/33R	CIE	R911	A
EZH 17	1965	Leyland Leopard PSU3/4R	CIE B45F	CIE	C17	A
EZH 64	1965	Leyland Leopard PSU3/4R	CIE/North East Health Board	CIE	C64	A
NZE 629	1965	Leyland Titan PD3A/3	Dundalk (Park Royal frame) O—/—R	CIE	R920	A
VZL 179	1966	Bedford VAL 14	Plaxton C53F	Wallace Arnold Tours, Leeds		A
EZH 231	1966	Leyland Leopard PSU3/4R	CIE B53F	CIE	C231	A
WZJ 724	1967	Bedford VAM 14	Duffy C45F	P O'Grady, Santry		A
EZL 1	1967	Bedford VAS 5	CIE B33F	CIE	SS1	RP
VZI 44	1967	Leyland Atlantean PDR1/1	CIE H43/35F	CIE	D44	A
note j	1972	Bedford VAL 70	Duffy B40D	Aer Lingus	301	A
694 ZO	1975	Leyland Atlantean AN68/1R	Van Hool H45/29D	CIE	D694	A
UZG 100	1984	Bombardier GAC	Bombardier B44D	CIE	KC100	A

Notes:

note i	Not registered	CYI 621	Breakdown vehicle
FRU 305	Originally numbered TD774; renumbered in 1950 and rebodied 1952	404 RIU	Originally registered VWG 376
		EZH 64	Originally B45F; converted to mobile hospital
IY 1940	Originally H38/26R; registered KTF 587	NZE 629	Originally H41/33R
ZL 2718	Ambulance conversion	VZL 179	Originally registered EUG 907D
ZJ 5933	Breakdown vehicle	note j	Not registered

Contact address: Cultra, Holywood, Co Down, BT18 OEU
Phone: 028 9042 8428
Affiliation: National Museums and Galleries of Northern Ireland
Brief description: A unique collection of wheeled vehicles from cycles to trams, railways, buses and cars. Interpretive exhibitions show the development of road transport. Not all the vehicles listed are always on display. Please enquire before your visit.
Opening days/times: All the year round but closing for a few days at Christmas time. From 09.30 or 10.30 on weekdays and 12.00 on Sundays (please 'phone for details)
Directions by car: On A2 Belfast-Bangor road.
Directions by public transport: On main Belfast-Bangor railway and bus routes.
Charges: £4 (discounts for groups)
Facilities: A D E F G L P R T

Registration	Date	Chassis	Body	New to	Fleet No	Status
CZ 7013	1935	Dennis Lancet I	Harkness B31F	Belfast Corporation	102	R
IL 2849	1937	Leyland Cheetah LZ1	(chassis only)	Erne Bus Co, Enniskillen		A
ZD 726	1941	GNR Gardner	Great Northern Railway (Ireland) B35F	Great Northern Railway (Ireland)	324	RP
GZ 1882	1944	Daimler CWA6	Harkness H30/26R	Belfast Corporation	214	A
GZ 4696	1946	Leyland Tiger PS1	(chassis only)	Northern Ireland Road Transport Board	Z800	A
FZ 7883+	1948	AEC 664T	Harkness/Park Royal H36/32R	Belfast Corporation	98	A
FZ 7897+	1948	Guy BTX	Harkness H36/32R	Belfast Corporation	112	R
EOI 4857	1973	Daimler Fleetline CRG6LX-33	Alexander, Belfast H49/37F	Belfast Corporation	857	R
KIJ 4035	1978	Dodge S56	Wright B25F	North Eastern Education & Library Board		A

+ Trolleybus

Notes:

ZD 726	Rebodied 1949
EOI 4857	Passed to Citybus (2857) in 1973; rebodied 1976

Amongst the many interesting buses which comprise the Ulster Folk & Transport Museum's collection is Harkness (1948)-bodied 1935 Dennis Lancet, Belfast 102. *Philip Lamb*

Contact address: Pacific Road, Birkenhead, Merseyside, L41 5HN
Phone: 0151 666 2756
Brief description: The museum houses a collection of buses, tramcars, motor cycles, cars and a few military vehicles. Some of the trams and buses are being restored by local enthusiast groups. Trams operate during weekends and some school holidays.

Opening days/times: Please telephone for details.
Directions by car: Adjacent to Woodside ferry terminal.
Directions by public transport: Bus or ferry to Woodside.
Other information: At the time of writing, the museum is closed for repairs, but is expected to open induring 2001 — please phone for details.

Registration	Date	Chassis	Body	New to	Fleet No	Status
BG 8557	1944	Guy Arab II	Massey H31/26R	Birkenhead Corporation	242	RP
BG 9225	1946	Leyland Titan PD1A	Massey H30/26R	Birkenhead Corporation	105	RP
GJB 279	1951	Bristol KSW6B	ECW L—/—RD	Thames Valley Traction Co	641	A
AHF 850	1951	Leyland Titan PD2/1	Metro Cammell H30/26R	Wallasey Corporation	54	R
RFM 641	1953	Guy Arab IV	Massey H30/26R	Chester Corporation	1	R
GM 5875	1953	Leyland Titan PD2/10	Leyland	Central SMT Co	L475	A
CHF 565	1956	Leyland Titan PD2/10	Burlingham H30/26R	Wallasey Corporation	106	RP
FHF 451	1958	Leyland Atlantean PRD1/1	Metro Cammell H44/33F	Wallasey Corporation	1	R
FBG 910	1958	Leyland Titan PD2/40	Massey H31/28R	Birkenhead Corporation	10	R
KFF 367	1962	AEC Routemaster R2RH	Park Royal H36/28R	London Transport	RM1101	R
RCM 493	1964	Leyland Leopard L1	Massey B42D	Birkenhead Corporation	93	R
GCM 152E	1967	Leyland Titan PD2/37	Massey H36/30R	Birkenhead Corporation	152	RP
UFM 52F	1968	Bristol RELL6G	ECW DP50F	Crosville Motor Services	ERG52	R
OFM 957K	1972	Daimler Fleetline CRG6LX	Northern Counties O43/29F	Chester Corporation	57	R
CWU 146T	1979	Leyland Fleetline FE30AGR	Roe H43/33F	West Yorkshire PTE	7146	R
XEM 898W	1981	Leyland Atlantean AN68B/1R	Alexander H43/32F	Merseyside PTE	1898	A

Notes:

BG 8557	Rebodied in 1953
GM 5875	Originally L27/26R; acquired by W Alexander & Sons (Midland) and converted to breakdown vehicle (ML245)
CHF 565	Carries 1949 body
KFF 367	Originally registered 101 CLT
OFM 957K	Originally H43/29F; rebodied 1984 and converted to open-top (renumbered 75) in 1998
CWU 146T	Promotional vehicle for The Hamilton Quarter. Currently H6/2FL.

The very first Leyland Atlantean to enter service was Wallasey No 1 in 1958. The Metro-Cammell-bodied bus is today a resident at Wirral Transport Museum, and is seen here in Birkenhead's Dockland. *Philip Lamb*

Part 2
Other Collections of Preserved Buses & Coaches

One of many non-West Midlands buses which form the West Midlands Preservation Society Collection is Bristol Omnibus 8322, a 1955 Bristol KSW6B, seen here outside the parish church at Aston, Birmingham.
Philip Lamb

Aldershot & District Bus Interest Group

Contact address: 111 Park Barn Drive, Guildford, Surrey, GU2 6ER
E-mail: website: sites.netscape.net/ashleyhoare
Affiliation: NARTM, FBHVC.
Brief description: The group was formed in 1994 to consolidate the collection of ex-Aldershot & District preserved vehicles and other artefacts which had been saved over the years. The vehicles range from 1920s Dennis E types to Dennis, AEC and Bristol buses which entered service in the 1960s and 1970s at the very end of the company's existence. The vehicles in the collection are in the care of

members of an associated group which also welcomes the owners of other preserved Dennis buses and coaches.
Events planned: Next running day May 2002. Please see press for details.
Opening days/times: Running days are held from time to time at which many of the operational vehicles may be seen in service.
Other information: Regular working parties; new members welcome.

Registration	Date	Chassis	Body	New to	Fleet No	Status
OT 8283	1928	Dennis E	(chassis only)	Aldershot & District Traction Co	D210	A
OT 8592	1928	Dennis E	Strachan & Brown	Aldershot & District Traction Co	D217	A
OT 8898	1928	Dennis E	Strachan & Brown	Aldershot & District Traction Co	D226	A
RD 111	1928	Dennis G	(unknown) T17	Reading Fire Brigade		R
OU 1805	1929	Dennis E	(chassis only)	Aldershot & District Traction Co	D283	A
TE 7870	1929	Dennis ES	Brush B29D	Accrington Corporation	57	R
CC 8671	1929	Dennis GL	Roberts T19	Llandudno UDC		R
CC 9424	1930	Dennis GL	Roberts T20	Llandudno UDC		A
MJ 4549	1932	Dennis Lancet I	Short B32F	Smith of Westoning		R
TJ 836	1933	Dennis Dart	Duple C20F	Entwhistle, Morcambe		R
JG 8720	1937	Dennis Lancet II	Park Royal B35R	East Kent Road Car Co		RP
GAA 580	1948	Dennis Lancet J3	Strachan B32R	Aldershot & District Traction Co	944	RP
GAA 616	1948	Dennis Lancet J3	Strachan C32R	Aldershot & District Traction Co	980	RP
GOU 845	1950	Dennis Lance K3	East Lancashire Coachbuilders L25/26R	Aldershot & District Traction Co	145	R
HOU 904	1950	Dennis Lancet J10	Strachan B38R	Aldershot & District Traction Co	178	R
LAA 231	1953	Dennis Lancet J10C	Strachan FC38R	Aldershot & District Traction Co	196	RP
MOR 581	1954	AEC Reliance MU3RV	Metro Cammell B40F	Aldershot & District Traction Co	543	R
LOU 48	1954	Dennis Lance K4	East Lancashire Coachbuilders L28/28R	Aldershot & District Traction Co	220	R
POR 428	1956	Dennis Falcon P5	Strachan B30F	Aldershot & District Traction Co	282	RP
SOU 456	1958	Dennis Loline	East Lancashire Coachbuilders H37/31RD	Aldershot & District Traction Co	348	RP
SOU 465	1958	Dennis Loline	East Lancashire Coachbuilders H37/31RD	Aldershot & District Traction Co	357	R
XHO 370	1960	AEC Reliance 2MU3RV	Weymann DP40F	Aldershot & District Traction Co	370	R
462 EOT	1962	Dennis Loline III	Alexander H39/29F	Aldershot & District Traction Co	462	RP
488 KOT	1964	Dennis Loline III	Weymann H39/29F	Aldershot & District Traction Co	488	RP
AAA 503C	1965	Dennis Loline III	Weymann H39/29F	Aldershot & District Traction Co	503	R
AAA 506C	1965	Dennis Loline III	Weymann H39/29F	Aldershot & District Traction Co	506	R
AAA 508C	1965	Dennis Loline III	Weymann H39/29F	Aldershot & District Traction Co	508	RP
CCG 296K	1971	Bristol RESL6G	ECW B40D	Aldershot & District Traction Co	651	RP

Notes:

OT 8283	Originally Dennis F, converted to E type		JG 8720	Rebodied 1949
RD 111	Replica body		MOR 581	Rebodied 1967
TE 7870	Body rebuilt 1974 by Wyatt			

Top right: Restored to early postwar livery is Aldershot & District 145, an East Lancs-bodied Dennis Lance K3, new in 1950. *Philip Lamb*

Right: Further buses comprising the Aldershot & District Bus Interest Group collection are from left to right: Weymann bodied Dennis Loline III, 503 and 1954 Dennis Lance K4, 220 and 1958 Dennis Loline 357, both with East Lancs bodywork. *Philip Lamb*

Aycliffe & District Bus Preservation Society

Contact address: 110 Fewston Close, Newton Aycliffe, Co Durham, DL5 7HF
Affiliation: NARTM; North East Museums Ltd.
Brief description: A collection of Darlington area service buses, the majority fully restored and in running order.
Events planned: -
Opening days/times: Viewing by prior appointment only.

Registration	Date	Chassis	Body	New to	Fleet No	Status
GHN 189	1942	Bristol K5G	ECW L27/26R	United Automobile Services	BGL29	R
LHN 860	1948	Bristol L5G	ECW B35F	United Automobile Services	BG413	R
304 GHN	1958	Bristol LS6G	ECW C39F	United Automobile Services	BUC4	RP
AHN 451B	1964	Daimler CCG5	Roe H32/31R	Darlington Corporation	7	R
NDL 769G	1969	Bristol LHS6L	Marshall B35F	Southern Vectis Omnibus Co	833	R

Notes:

GHN 189	1948 body fitted in 1954	304 GHN	Now fitted with Gardner engine
LHN 860	Converted to OMO c. 1955	NDL 769G	Acquired by United Automobile Services (1452) in 1977

Bolton Bus Group

Contact address: 12 Arundale, Westhoughton, Bolton BL5 3YB
Brief description: A small group of enthusiasts formed to preserve examples of Bolton's buses. Some of the vehicles are displayed at Bury Transport Museum, which can be visited by prior arrangement.
Opening days/times: Please write to the above address to arrange a visit.

Registration	Date	Chassis	Body	New to	Fleet No	Status
NBN 436	1959	Leyland Titan PD3/4	East Lancashire Coachbuilders H41/32F	Bolton Corporation	128	RP
SBN 767	1961	AEC Regent V 2D3RA	Metro Cammell H40/32F	Bolton Corporation	167	A
FBN 232C	1965	Leyland Atlantean PDR1/1	East Lancashire Coachbuilders H45/33F	Bolton Corporation	232	R
KUS 607E	1967	Leyland Atlantean PDR1/1	Alexander H44/34F	Glasgow Corporation	LA352	RP
TWH 809K	1971	Leyland Atlantean PDR2/1	East Lancashire Coachbuilders H49/37F	SELNEC PTE	6809	R

Flagship of the Bolton Bus Group is Bolton 232, an East Lancs-bodied Leyland Atlantean PDR1/1, seen here in its home town. *Philip Lamb*

Bournemouth Heritage Transport Collection

Phone: 01202 658333

Brief description: The collection comprises vehicles, mainly from Bournemouth Corporation or the Bournemouth area, built between the years 1928 and 1980. Most are owned by the Bournemouth Passenger Transport Association Ltd, which is a registered charity.

Events planned: Please see the enthusiast press for details.

Opening days/times: Owing to storage relocation, the collection is not currently open to the public. It is hoped to arrange an event during 2001. Please see the enthusiast press for details.

Registration	Date	Chassis	Body	New to	Fleet No	Status
RU 2266	1925	Shelvoke & Drewry Tramocar		Bournemouth Corporation	9	
LJ 500	1929	Karrier WL6/1	Hall Lewis B40D	Bournemouth Corporation	33	RP
VH 6188	1934	AEC Regent O661	Hall Lewis H—/—R	Huddersfield Corporation	119	A
VH 6217	1934	AEC Regent 661	Lee Motors	Huddersfield Corporation	120	R
BOW 162	1938	Bristol L5G	Hants+Dorset	Hants & Dorset Motor Services	9081	RP
DKY 711+	1944	Karrier W	East Lancashire Coachbuilders H37/29F	Bradford Corporation	711	A
DKY 712+	1944	Karrier W	East Lancashire Coachbuilders H37/29F	Bradford Corporation	712	A
HLJ 44	1948	Bristol K6A	ECW L27/28R	Hants & Dorset Motor Services	TD895	RP
NNU 234+	1949	BUT 9611T	Weymann H32/26R	Nottinghamshire & Derbyshire Traction Co	353	RP
JLJ 403	1949	Leyland Tiger PS2/3	Burlingham FDP35F	Bournemouth Corporation	46	R
KEL 110	1949	Leyland Titan PD2/3	Weymann FH33/25D	Bournemouth Corporation	110	R
KLJ 346+	1950	BUT 9641T	Weymann H31/25D	Bournemouth Corporation	212	R
KEL 127	1950	Leyland Titan PD2/3	Weymann FH33/25D	Bournemouth Corporation	127	
KEL 133	1950	Leyland Titan PD2/3	Weymann FH27/21D	Bournemouth Corporation	247	R
MOD 978	1952	Bristol LS6G	East Lancashire Coachbuilders	Royal Blue	1291	
NLJ 268	1953	Leyland Royal Tiger PSU1/13	Burlingham B42F	Bournemouth Corporation	258	R
NLJ 272	1953	Leyland Royal Tiger PSU1/13	Burlingham B42F	Bournemouth Corporation	262	R
RRU 901	1955	Leyland Tiger Cub PSUC1/1	Park Royal B42F	Bournemouth Corporation	264	R
RRU 904	1955	Leyland Tiger Cub PSUC1/1	Park Royal B42F	Bournemouth Corporation	267	R
YLJ 147	1959	Leyland Titan PD3/1	Weymann H37/25D	Bournemouth Corporation	147	R
8154 EL	1960	Leyland Titan PD3/1	Weymann H37/25D	Bournemouth Corporation	154	R
8156 EL	1960	Leyland Titan PD3/1	Weymann O37/25D	Bournemouth Corporation	156	R
8159 EL	1960	Leyland Titan PD3/1	Weymann H37/25D	Bournemouth Corporation	159	
NMR 345	1960	Leyland Titan PD3/1	Weymann H37/25D	Bournemouth Corporation	155	RP
297 LJ+	1962	Sunbeam MF2B	Weymann H37/28D	Bournemouth Corporation	297	R
6162 RU	1963	Leyland Titan PD3A/1	Weymann H39/30F	Bournemouth Corporation	162	R
6167 RU	1963	Leyland Titan PD3A/1	Weymann H39/30F	Bournemouth Corporation	167	R
ALJ 340B	1964	Daimler Fleetline CRG6LX	M H Cars H44/33F	Bournemouth Corporation	40	R
AEL 170B	1964	Leyland Atlantean PDR1/1	Weymann H43/31F	Bournemouth Corporation	170	R
CRU 180C	1965	Daimler Fleetline CRG6LX	Weymann CO43/31F	Bournemouth Corporation	180	R
CRU 187C	1965	Daimler Fleetline CRG6LX	Weymann CO43/31F	Bournemouth Corporation	187	
CRU 103C	1965	Leyland Leopard PSU3/2R	Weymann DP45F	Bournemouth Corporation	103	R
ERV 247D	1966	Leyland Atlantean PDR1/1	MCW O43/33F	Portsmouth Corporation	247	RP
ERV 249D	1966	Leyland Atlantean PDR1/1	MCW O43/33F	Portsmouth Corporation	249	
ERV 251D	1966	Leyland Atlantean PDR1/1	MCW O43/33F	Portsmouth Corporation	251	
ERV 252D	1966	Leyland Atlantean PDR1/1	MCW O43/33F	Portsmouth Corporation	252	
KRU 55F	1967	Daimler Roadliner SRC6	Willowbrook B49F	Bournemouth Corporation	55	R
FJY 915E	1967	Leyland Atlantean PDR1/1	MCW O43/32F	Plymouth Corporation	215	RP
ORU 230G	1969	Leyland Atlantean PDR1A/1	Alexander H43/31F	Bournemouth Corporation	230	R
VRU 124J	1971	Daimler Fleetline CRG6LXB	Roe H43/31F	Hants & Dorset Motor Services	1901	R
DLJ 111L	1972	Daimler Fleetline CRL6	Alexander O43/31F	Bournemouth Corporation	111	R
DLJ 116L	1972	Daimler Fleetline CRL6	Alexander H43/31F	Bournemouth Corporation	116	R
DLJ 119L	1972	Daimler Fleetline CRL6	Alexander H43/31F	Bournemouth Corporation	119	A
XRU 277K	1972	Leyland Atlantean PDR1A/1	Alexander H43/31F	Bournemouth Corporation	277	RP

Registration	Date	Chassis	Body	New to	Fleet No	Status
FEL 105L	1973	Leyland Leopard PSU3B/4R	Plaxton C47F	Bournemouth Corporation	105	A
FLG 209V	1980	Dodge	18 seats	Bournemouth Corporation	M9	
+Trolleybus						

Notes:

RU 2266	Chassis and axles only	NLJ 268	Originally B42F; used as canteen at Chesterfield 1970-81
8159 EL	Converted to mobile museum		
VH 6188	Chassis new 1934, fitted with 1928 body	NMR 345	Originally registered 8155 EL
VH 6217	Converted to tower wagon in 1948	ERV 247D	Originally H43/33F
BOW 162	New with Beadle body; converted to breakdown vehicle	FJY 915E	Originally H43/32F
DKY 711	Rebodied 1960	DLJ 111L	Originally H43/31F
DKY 712	Rebodied 1960	FLG 209V	Battery Bus

Bristol Vintage Bus Group

Contact address: 74 Ridgeway Lane, Whitchurch, Bristol BS14 9PJ
Location: Unit G, Flowers Hill Road, Brislington, Bristol
Brief description: A small group of enthusiasts formed to preserve examples of Bristol's buses.
Events planned: 19 August 2001 open day with vehicles running trips
Opening days/times: At any time by prior arrangement if someone is available.

Directions by car: Flowers Hill Road is off the A4 Bath road, right on the City boundary near the Park & Ride.
Directions by public transport: Main bus service to Bath from the Bus Station and Temple Meads railway station stops near Flowers Hill Road.
Charges: No admission charge for viewing or special events.

Registration	Date	Chassis	Body	New to	Fleet No	Status
AHU 803	1934	Bristol J5G	Brislington Body Works B35R	Bristol Tramways & Carriage Co	2355	R
GHT 154	1940	Bristol K5G	Brislington Body Works H30/26R	Bristol Tramways & Carriage Co	C3336	R
FTT 704	1945	Bristol K6A	ECW L27/28R	Western National Omnibus Co	353	R
LAE 13	1948	Leyland PD1A	ECW H30/26R	Bristol Tramways & Carriage Co	C4044	R
YHY 80	1957	Bristol LS6G	ECW B43F	Bristol Omnibus Co	3004	RP

Notes:

AHU 803	Rebodied 1947. Originally a petrol engined coach.
FTT 704	Original Strachans body replaced in 1955.

Seen in Bristol in 2000 were 1934 Bristol J5G, Bristol Tramways 2355, rebodied by BBW in 1947 and from the same fleet No C3336, a 1940 BBW-bodied Bristol K5G. *Philip Lamb*

British Trolleybus Society

Contact address: 8 Riding Lane, Hildenborough, Tonbridge, Kent, TN11 9HX
Brief description: The British Trolleybus Society is a contributor society to the Sandtoft Transport Centre. Vehicles from the collection of trolleybuses can be seen from time to time at Sandtoft on display.
Events planned: Details given in the section on Sandtoft Transport Centre.

Registration	Date	Chassis	Body	New to	Fleet No	Status
WW 4688+	1927	Garrett O type	Garrett B32C	Mexborough & Swinton Traction Co 34		A
RD 7127	1935	AEC Regent II O661	Park Royal L26/26R	Reading Corporation	47	R
ALJ 973+	1935	Sunbeam MS2	Park Royal H31/25D	Bournemouth Corporation	99	RP
CU 3593+	1937	Karrier E4	Weymann H29/26R	South Shields Corporation	204	A
ARD 676+	1939	AEC 661T	Park Royal H30/26R	Reading Corporation	113	R
CKG 193+	1942	AEC 664T	Northern Counties H38/32R	Cardiff Corporation	203	A
HYM 812+	1948	BUT 9641T	Metro Cammell H40/30R	London Transport	1812	RP
NDH 959+	1951	Sunbeam F4	Brush H34/31R	Walsall Corporation	342	RP
AC-L 379+	1956	Henschel 562E	Ludewig RB17/44T	Aachen (Germany)	22	RP
XDH 72+	1956	Sunbeam F4A	Willowbrook H36/34RD	Walsall Corporation	872	R
FYS 839+	1958	BUT 9613T	Crossley H37/34R	Glasgow Corporation	TB78	R
PVH 931+	1959	Sunbeam S7A	East Lancashire Coachbuilders H40/32R	Huddersfield Corporation	631	R
+Trolleybus						

Notes:

NDH 959	Rebuilt/lengthened 1965
AC-L 379	German registration
XDH 72	Last Walsall trolleybus; on display at Aston Manor Road Transport Museum.

Cardiff & South Wales Trolleybus Project

Contact address: 211 Hillrise, Llanedeyrn, Cardiff CF23 6UQ
Affiliation: NARTM
Brief description: The only trolleybus preservation group in the principality of Wales. A regular newsletter is issued, and new members are always welcome.

Registration	Date	Chassis	Body	New to	Fleet No	Status
DKY 704+	1945	Karrier W	East Lancashire Coachbuilders H37/29F	Bradford Corporation	704	RP
EBO 919+	1949	BUT 9641T	Bruce H38/29D	Cardiff Corporation	262	RP
KBO 961+	1955	BUT 9641T	East Lancashire Coachbuilders B40R	Cardiff Corporation	243	A
DHW 293K	1972	Bristol LH6L	ECW B42F	Bristol Omnibus Co	353	
+Trolleybus						

Notes:

DKY 704	Rebodied in 1959
EBO 919	Body built on East Lancs frames
DHW 293K	Support vehicle

Chelveston Preservation Society

Contact address: 36 Moor Road, Rushden, Northants, NN10 9SP
Brief description: The group has its origins with a small number of employees of United Counties. The collection has evolved to represent most types of Bristol chassis from a range of former Tilling group companies.

Registration	Date	Chassis	Body	New to	Fleet No	Status
VV 5696	1937	Bristol JO5G	ECW B35R	United Counties Omnibus Co	450	R
MPU 21	1948	Bristol K6B	ECW L27/28R	Eastern National Omnibus Co	3960	RP
HPW 108	1949	Bristol K5G	ECW H30/26R	Eastern Counties Omnibus Co	LKH108	A
NAE 3	1950	Bristol L6B	ECW FC31F	Bristol Tramways & Carriage Co	2467	RP
HWV 294	1952	Bristol KSW5G	ECW L27/28R	Wilts & Dorset	365	A
CNH 860	1952	Bristol LWL5G	ECW B39R	United Counties Omnibus Co	426	R
CNH 862	1952	Bristol LWL6B	ECW DP33R	United Counties Omnibus Co	428	R
KNV 337	1954	Bristol KSW6B	ECW L27/28R	United Counties Omnibus Co	964	R
RFM 408	1954	Bristol Lodekka LD6B	ECW H33/25R	Crosville Motor Services	ML663	A
TUO 497	1956	Bristol LS6G	ECW B45F	Southern National Omnibus Co	1781	RP
VVF 543	1957	Bristol SC4LK	ECW B35F	Eastern Counties Omnibus Co	LC543	RP
RFU 689	1958	Bristol SC4LK	ECW DP33F	Lincolnshire Road Car Co	2611	R
OPN 807	1959	Bristol Lodekka LDS6B	ECW H33/27R	Brighton Hove & District Omnibus Co	7	A
675 COD	1960	Bristol SUS4A	ECW B30F	Western National Omnibus Co	603	A
827 BWY	1963	Bristol MW6G	ECW B45F	West Yorkshire Road Car Co	SMG19	RP
375 GWN	1964	Bristol RELL6G	ECW C47F	United Welsh Services	52	A
DEL 893C	1965	Bristol Lodekka FLF6G	ECW H38/32F	Hants & Dorset Motor Services	1220	A
GAX 2C	1965	Bristol RELL6G	ECW B54F	Red & White Services	R2 65	RP
OWC 182D	1966	Bristol MW6G	ECW C34F	Tilling Transport	182	R
EDV 555D	1966	Bristol SUL4A	ECW B36F	Southern National Omnibus Co	692	RP
OAX 9F	1968	Bristol RELH6G	ECW C47F	Red & White Services	RC968	R
MMW 354G	1969	Bristol RELL6G	ECW B45D	Wilts & Dorset	824	R
SGF 483L	1970	Bristol RELH6L	PLAXTON C5IF	Isle of Man Road Services		A
HAH 537L	1972	Bristol LH6P	ECW B45F	Eastern Counties Omnibus Co	LH537	RP

Notes:

VV 5696	Rebodied 1949
CNH 860	Renumbered 426 in 1952; Gardner 5LW engine fitted 1956
CNH 862	Gardner 5LW engine fitted in 1956. Reverted to Bristol AVW in 1996.
RFM 408	Eighth production lodekka. Currently has no engine or gearbox
OWC 182D	Passed to Eastern National (392) in 1968 and to Tilling's Travel (9392) in 1971
SGF 483L	Originally registered 40 WMN

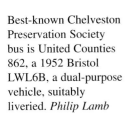

Best-known Chelveston Preservation Society bus is United Counties 862, a 1952 Bristol LWL6B, a dual-purpose vehicle, suitably liveried. *Philip Lamb*

Cherwell Bus Preservation Group

Contact address: 17 Andersons Close, Kidlington, Oxford OX5 1ST
Brief description: A collection of mainly ex-City of Oxford vehicles housed under cover.

Events planned: The operational vehicles will attend a few events during the rally season.

Registration	Date	Chassis	Body	New to	Fleet No	Status
OJO 727	1950	AEC Regal III 9621A	Willowbrook B32F	City of Oxford Motor Services	727	R
191 AWL	1956	AEC Regent V MD3RV	Weymann L30/26R	City of Oxford Motor Services	L191	R
194 BFC	1957	AEC Regent V MD3RV	Weymann L30/28RD	City of Oxford Motor Services	L194	A
975 CWL	1958	AEC Regent V LD3RA	Park Royal H37/28R	City of Oxford Motor Services	H975	RP
312 MFC	1961	AEC Bridgemaster 2B3RA	Park Royal H43/29F	City of Oxford Motor Services	312	RP
324 NJO	1962	AEC Bridgemaster 2B3RA	Park Royal H40/25F	City of Oxford Motor Services	324	A
332 RJO	1963	AEC Renown 3B3RA	Park Royal H38/27F	City of Oxford Motor Services	332	RP
340 TJO	1964	AEC Renown 3B3RA	Park Royal H38/27F	City of Oxford Motor Services	340	A
OFC 902H	1970	Bristol VRTSL6LX	ECW H39/31F	City of Oxford Motor Services	902	RP
VUD 348H	1970	Leyland Leopard	Plaxton Elite	Heyfordian, Upper Heyford		A
AUD 310J	1971	Leyland Leopard	Plaxton Elite II	Slatters, Long Hanborough		A
YWL 134K	1972	Leyland Leopard	Plaxton Elite II	Jarvis, Middle Barton		A
TJO 56K	1972	AEC Reliance 6MU4R	Marshall DP49F	City of Oxford Motor Services	56	A
NUD 105L	1973	Bristol VRTSL6LX	ECW CH41/27F	City of Oxford Motor Services	105	A
RBW 87M	1974	Bristol RELH6L	ECW DP49F	City of Oxford Motor Services	87	A
PWL 999W	1980	Leyland Olympian B45/TL11/2R	Alexander H50/32D	Leyland demonstrator		A
VJO 201X	1982	Leyland Olympian ONLXB/1R	ECW H45/27D	City of Oxford Motor Services	201	A
VUD 30X	1982	Leyland Leopard PSU3G/4R	ECW C49F	City of Oxford Motor Services	30	A
C729 JJO	1986	Ford Transit 190D	Carlyle DP20F	City of Oxford Motor Services	729	A

Notes:

PWL 999W   Leyland Olympian prototype built as Far East demonstrator and operated by Singapore Bus Services registered SBS 5396B; later fitted with Gardner engine and acquired by City of Oxford Motor Services (999) in 1987

Chesterfield 123 Group

Contact address: 87 Broom Drive, Grassmoor, Chesterfield, Derbyshire, S42 5AH

Brief description: The group owns the small collection of Chesterfield vehicles listed, which are shown at rallies throughout the season.

Registration	Date	Chassis	Body	New to	Fleet No	Status
PNU 114K	1971	Leyland Atlantean	Northern Counties	Chesterfield Corporation	114	RP
NNU 123M	1973	Daimler Fleetline CRL6-30	Roe H42/29D	Chesterfield Corporation	123	R
NNU 124M	1973	Daimler Fleetline CRL6-30	Roe H42/29D	Chesterfield Corporation	124	R

Formerly at the Oxford Bus Museum, 1956 Weymanbodied AEC Regent V, City of Oxford L191 is part of the newly-formed Cherwell Bus Preservation Group collection. *Philip Lamb*

The Devon General Society

Contact address: Membership Secretary, Greenfields, The Rowe, Stableford, Newcastle-under-Lyme, Staffs ST5 4EN
Brief description: The Devon General Society was formed in 1982 to promote interest in the former Devon General company and its successors, also to stimulate the preservation of all aspects of the company's past for the benefit of future generations. Approximately

35 former Devon General vehicles are currently preserved privately by society members, The society actively assists them and regularly stages events in Devon whereby these vehicles can be enjoyed.
Events planned: 13 May 2001 — Torbay Classic Bus & Coach Gathering, Oldway Mansion, Paignton

Registration	Date	Chassis	Body	New to	Fleet No	Status
OD 7497	1934	AEC Regent I O661	Short O31/24R	Devon General Omnibus & Touring Co	DR210	RP
HTT 487	1946	AEC Regal I O662	Weymann B35F	Devon General Omnibus & Touring Co	SR487	R
KOD 585	1949	AEC Regent III 9612E	Weymann H30/26R	Devon General Omnibus & Touring Co	DR585	RP
MTT 640	1951	Leyland Titan PD2/1	Leyland L27/26R	Devon General Omnibus & Touring Co	DL640	R
NTT 661	1952	AEC Regent III 9613A	Weymann H30/26R	Devon General Omnibus & Touring Co	DR661	R
NTT 679	1952	AEC Regent III 9613S	Weymann H30/26R	Devon General Omnibus & Touring Co	DR679	R
TTT 781	1956	AEC Regent V MD3RV	Metro Cammell H33/26RD	Devon General Omnibus & Touring Co	DRD781	RP
VDV 817	1957	AEC Regent V MD3RV	Metro Cammell H33/26R	Devon General Omnibus & Touring Co	DR817	R
VDV 798	1957	AEC Reliance MU3RA	Weymann B41F	Devon General Omnibus & Touring Co	SR798	A
UFJ 296	1957	Guy Arab IV	Park Royal H31/26R	Exeter City Transport	56	R
XTA 839	1958	Albion Nimbus NS3N	Willowbrook B31F	Devon General Omnibus & Touring Co	SN839	A
XUO 721	1958	Bristol MW6G	ECW B41F	Western National Omnibus Co (Royal Blue)	2902	R
872 ATA	1959	Leyland Atlantean PDR1/1	MCW H44/32F	Devon General Omnibus & Touring Co	DL872	RP
913 DTT	1960	Leyland Atlantean PDR1/1	Roe H43/31F	Devon General Omnibus & Touring Co	DL913	A
935 GTA	1961	AEC Reliance 2MU3RV	Willowbrook C41F	Devon General Grey Cars	TCR935	R
931 GTA	1961	Leyland Atlantean PDR1/1	Metro Cammell CO44/31F	Devon General Omnibus & Touring Co	DL931	R
932 GTA	1961	Leyland Atlantean PDR1/1	Metro Cammell CO44/31F	Devon General Omnibus & Touring Co	DL932	R
960 HTT	1962	AEC Reliance 2MU3RV	Willowbrook C41F	Devon General Grey Cars Touring Co	TCR960	R
503 RUO	1964	AEC REGENT V 2D3RA	Willowbrook H39/30F	Devon General Omnibus & Touring Co	503	RP
9 RDV	1964	AEC Reliance 2U3RA	Marshall B49F	Devon General Omnibus & Touring Co	9	R
CTT 23C	1965	AEC Reliance 2MU3RA	Park Royal B39F	Devon General Omnibus & Touring Co	23	R
LUO 47F	1968	AEC Reliance 6U3ZR	Willowbrook DP47F	Devon General Omnibus & Touring Co	47	R
NDV 537G	1968	Leyland Atlantean PDR1/2	Metro Cammell H44/31F	Devon General Omnibus & Touring Co	537	R
TUO 74J	1970	AEC Reliance 6MU3R	Willowbrook B41F	Devon General Omnibus & Touring Co	74	RP
VOD 550K	1971	Bristol VRT/SL2/6G	ECW H43/31F	Devon General Omnibus & Touring Co	550	RP

Registration	Date	Chassis	Body	New to	Fleet No	Status
VOD 107S	1978	Bristol LH6L	ECW B43F	Devon General Omnibus & Touring Co	127	RP
C519 FFJ	1985	Ford Transit 1 160	Carlyle B16F	Devon General Bayline	519	R
E815 WDV	1986	Ford Transit Mk II	Mellor B16F	Devon General Omnibus & Touring Co	815	R

Note:

OD 7497   Converted to open top in 1955

Right: Devon General's 'Sea Dog' class, formed of convertible Metro-Cammell-bodied Leyland Atlanteans of 1961, are notable survivors. Here we see DL931 *Sir Thomas Howard* restored to its National Bus Company era identity.
Philip Lamb

Below: New as Western National 550, but restored as a Devon General vehicle, this Bristol VRTSL2 was captured at Poole in 1997.
Philip Lamb

Dewsbury Bus Museum

Contact address: Mr Deakin, 5 Oakenshaw Street, Agbrigg, Wakefield WF1 5BT

Brief description: The group was formed in the early 1970s and concentrated on ex-West Riding vehicles. By 1989 the collection had grown and, to provide covered accommodation, a new, 14-vehicle shed was erected. Vehicles can be seen at local events, or on site by appointment.

Opening days/times: Open only on rally days and when work is being done on vehicles (please enquire before visiting).

Other information: Other events are being planned — please see enthusiast press for details.

Registration	Date	Chassis	Body	New to	Fleet No	Status
TY 9608	1932	AEC Regal 662	Strachan C28R	Orange Bros, Bedlington	42	A
DHN 475	1939	Bristol L5G	ECW B35R	United Automobile Services	BLO 11	A
AHL 694	1947	Leyland Tiger PS1/1	Barnaby B35F	J Bullock & Sons, Featherstone	284	RP
BHL 682	1948	Leyland Titan PD2/1	Leyland L27/26R	West Riding Automobile Co	640	RP
TWY 8	1950	Albion CX39N	Roe L27/26RD	South Yorkshire Motors	81	RP
NHU 2	1951	Bristol LSX5G	ECW B44F	Bristol Tramways & Carriage Co	2800	RP
EHL 344	1952	Leyland Tiger PS2/12A	Roe B39F	West Riding Automobile Co	733	R
EHL 336	1952	Leyland Tiger PS2/13A	Roe C35F	West Riding Automobile Co	725	A
JHL 708	1956	AEC Reliance MU3RV	Roe B44F	West Riding Automobile Co	808	RP
JHL 983	1957	AEC Reliance MU3RV	Roe C41C	West Riding Automobile Co	803	R
KHL 855	1957	Guy Arab IV	Roe L29/26RD	West Riding Automobile Co	855	RP
924 AHY	1958	Bristol MW5G	ECW B45F	Bristol Omnibus Co	2934	RP
TWT 123	1958	Bristol MW5G	ECW DP41F	West Yorkshire Road Car Co	EUG 71	RP
5228 NW	1959	Leyland Titan PD3/5	Roe H38/32R	Leeds City Transport	228	A
LEN 101	1960	Guy Wulfrunian	(chassis only)	Bury Corporation	101	A
574 CNW	1962	Daimler CVG6	Roe H39/31F	Leeds City Transport	574	RP
PJX 35	1962	Leyland Leopard L1	Weymann B42F	Halifax Corporation	35	R
WHL 970	1963	Guy Wulfrunian	Roe H43/32F	West Riding Automobile Co	970	A
CUV 208C	1965	AEC Routemaster R2RH	Park Royal H38/28R	London Transport	RM2208	R
LHL 164F	1967	Leyland Panther PSUR1/1	Roe B51F	West Riding Automobile Co	164	R
THL 261H	1970	Bristol RELL6G	ECW B53F	West Riding Automobile Co	261	RP
TDL 567K	1971	Bristol RELL6G	ECW B53F	Southern Vectis Omnibus Co	867	A
MCK 229J	1971	Leyland Panther PSUR1B/1R	Pennine B47D	Preston Corporation	229	RP
WEX 685M	1973	AEC Swift 3MP2R	ECW B43D	Great Yarmouth Corporation	85	RP
MUA 865P	1976	Leyland Atlantean AN68/1R	Roe H43/30F	Yorkshire Woollen District Transport Co	768	R

Notes:

TWY 8	New in 1950, registered JWT 112; rebodied and reregistered in 1958
NHU 2	Prototype Bristol LS
MUA 865P	Rebodied 1981

Based a long way from its London home is Malcolm King's Shillibeer-liveried AEC Routemaster RM2208, a Dewsbury Bus Museum resident. *Philip Lamb*

East Pennine Transport Group

Contact address: 23 George Street, Lindley, Huddersfield HD3 3LY
Affiliation: Transport Trust; Keighley Bus Museum
Brief description: An active group progressing with the restoration of a number of interesting vehicles. Please write to the Huddersfield address if you wish to arrange a visit.

Events planned: 12 August 2001 — Kirklees Historic Vehicle Parade.
Opening days/times: Visits to workshop only; strictly by prior arrangement.

Registration	Date	Chassis	Body	New to	Fleet No	Status
BRM 596	1936	Leyland Titan TD4	ECW L27/28R	Cumberland Motor Services	291	RP
AVH 470+	1938	Karrier E6	Park Royal H36/28R	Huddersfield Corporation	470	A
CCX 777	1945	Daimler CWA6	Duple L27/28R	Huddersfield Joint Omnibus Committee	217	RP
CCX 801	1945	Guy Arab II	Roe L27/26R	County Motors, Lepton	70	RP
FVH 1	1951	Guy Arab UF	Park Royal B43F	Huddersfield Joint Omnibus Committee	1	RP
HVH 234	1954	AEC Regent III 9613E	East Lancashire Coachbuilders L30/28R	Huddersfield Joint Omnibus Committee	234	RP
8340 U	1958	Leyland Tiger Cub PSUC1/2	Burlingham C41F	Wallace Arnold Tours, Leeds		RP
CBA 966L	1973	Bedford J2SZ2	Plaxton C15F	Salford Social Services		R
+ Trolleybus						

Notes:
BRM 596   Rebodied 1950
CCX 801   Rebodied 1955

Friends of King Alfred Buses

Contact address: 27 White Dirt Lane, Catherington, Waterlooville, Hampshire, PO8 ONB
E-mail: FOKABevents@lineone.net
Brief description: The collection includes 12 former King Alfred Motor Services vehicles that have been rescued from around the world and restored. A charitable trust, FoKAB aims eventually to establish a museum. In the meantime, the vehicles can be viewed at the annual running day and other events.
Events planned: 1 Jan 2002 — Annual running day at Winchester.

Registration	Date	Chassis	Body	New to	Fleet No	Status
OU 9286	1931	Dennis 30cwt	Short B18F	King Alfred Motor Services		R
HOR 493	1949	Leyland Titan PD2/1	Leyland H30/26R	Isle of Man Road Services	72	A
JAA 708	1950	Leyland Olympic HR40	MCW B40F	King Alfred Motor Services		RP
POU 494	1956	Leyland Titan PD2/24	East Lancashire Coachbuilders L27/28R	King Alfred Motor Services		R
WCG 104	1959	Leyland Tiger Cub PSUC1/1	Weymann B45F	King Alfred Motor Services		R
326 CAA	1961	Bedford SB3	Harrington C41F	King Alfred Motor Services		R
595 LCG	1964	AEC Renown 3B2RA	Park Royal H43/31F	King Alfred Motor Services		R
596 LCG	1964	AEC Renown 3B2RA	Park Royal H43/31F	King Alfred Motor Services		R
CCG 704C	1965	Bedford VAL 14	Plaxton C49F	King Alfred Motor Services		RP
HOR 590E	1967	Leyland Atlantean PDR1/2	Roe O43/31F	King Alfred Motor Services		R
HOR 592E	1967	Leyland Atlantean PDR1/2	Roe H43/33F	King Alfred Motor Services		R
UOU 417H	1970	Leyland Panther PSUR1A/1R	Plaxton B52F	King Alfred Motor Services		R
UOU 419H	1970	Leyland Panther PSUR1A/1R	Plaxton B52F	King Alfred Motor Services		R
YDW 756K	1972	Metro-Scania BR111MH	MCW B40D	Newport Corporation	56	RP

Notes:

HOR 493	To be restored as King Alfred vehicle; originally registered KMN 502
POU 494	Repatriated from the USA in 1993
595 LCG	On loan from the Oxford Bus Museum
596 LCG	Repatriated from the USA in 1988

HOR 590E	Originally H43/33F; acquired by Bristol Omnibus Co (8602) and converted to open-top in 1979
HOR 592E	Acquired by Bristol Omnibus Co (8600) and converted to open-top in 1979; restored using roof from sister vehicle HOR591E

Another 'new' museum established in 2000 was the Glasgow Bus Museum. The collection includes Glasgow L163, a 1958 Leyland PD2/24 with Alexander bodywork.

Glasgow Bus Museum

Contact address: Bay E North, Barclay Curle Complex, 139 South Street, Glasgow G14 0AN
Phone: 0141 954 5400

Fax: 0141 954 5401
Events planned: 25/26 August 2001 — Open Weekend.

Registration	Date	Chassis	Body	New to	Fleet No	Status
BUS 181	1938	AEC Regent III O661	Tow Wagon	Glasgow Corporation	AR292	
HUS 675	1950	Albion Victor FT21N	Bennett B20F	Glasgow Education	BS1	
HUS 676	1950	Albion Victor FT21N	Bennett B20F	Glasgow Education	BS2	
FYS 996+	1958	BUT RETB1	Burlingham B50F	Glasgow Corporation	TBS21	
FYS 999	1958	Daimler CVD6-30	Alexander H41/32R	Glasgow Corporation	D217	
SGD 65	1958	Leyland Titan PD2/24	Alexander H33/28R	Glasgow Corporation	L163	
SGD 239	1959	Daimler CVG6 2D2RA	Alexander H33/28R	Glasgow Corporation	D256	
SGD 241	1959	Daimler CVG6 2D2RA	Alexander H33/28R	Glasgow Corporation	D258	
SGD 491	1960	AEC Regent V	Alexander H-/-R	Glasgow Corporation	A341	
SGD 448	1961	Leyland Titan PD3/2	Alexander H41/31R	Glasgow Corporation	L446	
SGD 500	1961	AEC Regent V	Alexander H43/31R	Glasgow Corporation	A350	
WLT 759	1961	AEC Routemaster R2RH	Park Royal H36/28R	London Transport	RM759	
VML 5G	1969	Leyland Atlantean PDR2/1	Park Royal H-/-R	Road transport Industry Training Board	-	
XGA 8J	1969	Leyland Atlantean	Alexander H45/29F	Glasgow Corporation	LA510	
HGD 894L	1973	Leyland Atlantean AN68/1R	Alexander H45/29F	Glasgow Corporation	LA688	
GGG 300N	1975	Ailsa B55-10	Alexander H44/35F	Greater Glasgow PTE	AV1	
FSU 102T	1979	Leyland Atlantean AN68A/1R	Alexander H45/33F	Greater Glasgow PTE	LA1285	
RDS 597W	1980	Leyland Atlantean AN68A/1R	Alexander H45/33F	Greater GlasgowPTE	LA1408	
UGB 193W	1981	Leyland Atlantean AN68A/1R	Alexander H45/33F	Strathclyde PTE	LA1440	
CUS 297X	1981	Leyland Atlantean AN68A/1R	Alexander H45/33F	Strathclyde PTE	LA1442	
UGB 196W	1981	Leyland Atlantean AN68A/1R	Alexander H45/33F	Strathclyde PTE	LA1443	
CUS 302X	1981	Leyland Atlantean AN68A/1R	Alexander H45/33F	Strathclyde PTE	LA1448	

+Trolleybus

Golcar Transport Collection

Contact address: 45 Cowlersley Lane, Cowlersley, Huddersfield HD4 5TZ
Brief description: A unique collection of Karrier vehicles, most of which are long-term restoration projects. The collection includes two WL6 six-wheeled saloons.
Opening days/times: Collection opens to coincide with craft weekends at the Colne Valley Museum in Lancashire; can be opened at other times by prior arrangement.

Registration	Date	Chassis	Body	New to	Fleet No	Status
note v	1922	Karrier	(unknown) B20F	(unknown)		A
WT 9156	1925	Karrier JH	Strachan & Brown B26F	Premier Transport, Keighley		RP
DY 5029	1928	Karrier JKL	London Lorries C26D	A Timpson & Son, Catford	117	A
KD 3185	1928	Karrier WL6	Liverpool Corporation B38R	Liverpool Corporation		A
TE 5780	1928	Karrier WL6	English Electric B32F	Ashton under Lyne Corporation	8	RP
VH 2088	1929	Karrier ZA	(unknown) B14F			RP
RB 4757	1932	Commer Centaur	Reeve & Kenning B14D	H G Fox, Alfreton		RP
JC 5313	1938	Guy Wolf	Waveney C20F	Llandudno UDC		R
14 PKR	1961	Karrier BFD	Plaxton C14F	W Davis & Sons, Sevenoaks		A

Notes:

note v	Unregistered solid-tyred, disc-wheeled chassis.
WT 9156	Body originally on EH 4960
VH 2088	Period body acquired from Anglesey
RB 4757	Carries 1929 body from Ford AA chassis

Huddersfield Passenger Transport Group

Contact address: 20 Alma Drive, Dalton, Huddersfield HD5 9EF
Brief description: The collection is based in Huddersfield and comprises nearly 20 vehicles, including commercial vehicles and trams.

There are currently six buses in the collection.
Opening days/times: Please contact the above address for an appointment to view.

Registration	Date	Chassis	Body	New to	Fleet No	Status
ECX 425	1949	AEC Regent III 9612E	Northern Coach Builders L29/26R	Huddersfield Joint Omnibus Committee	225	RP
EFV 300	1951	Leyland Titan PD2/5	Burlingham FH29/23C	Blackpool Corporation	300	RP
ODE 182	1952	Sentinel STC6	Sentinel B44F	Edwards Bros, Crimich		RP
HVH 472D	1966	Daimler CVG6LX-30	East Lancashire Coachbuilders H41/29F	Huddersfield Corporation	472	R
JWU 244N	1974	Leyland Leopard PSU4C/4R	Plaxton B43F	West Yorkshire PTE	8501	RP

Notes:
JWU 244N   Owned by the National Coalmining Museum, Wakefield

The Huddersfield Passenger Transport Group regularly rallies Huddersfield 472, an East Lancs-bodied Daimler CVG6. *Philip Lamb*

Kelvin Amos Collection

Contact address: 30 Blandford Close, Nailsea, Bristol BS48 2QQ
Brief description: The two vehicles in the collection are regularly
shown and run on free bus services.

Registration	Date	Chassis	Body	New to	Fleet No	Status
LHT 911	1948	Bristol L5G	Brislington Body Works B35R	Bristol Tramways & Carriage Co	2388	R
KED 546F	1968	Leyland Panther Cub	East Lancashire Coachbuilders B41D	Warrington Corporation	92	R

Notes:
LHT 911   Rebodied 1958 with 1950 body

Seen here at Bristol Docks is Bristol Tramways 2388, Kelvin Amos's BBW-bodied Bristol L5G of 1948 vintage.
Philip Lamb

Lancastrian Transport Trust

Contact address: 1 Beverley Grove, South Shore, Blackpool, Lancashire FY4 2BG
E-mail: philip@ltt.org.uk
Web site: www.ltt.org.ou
Brief description: The trust is dedicated to preserving historic

buses from Lancashire. Vehicles can often be seen at local rallies and other events.
Membership details: Support organisation is TransSupport with a £10 annual membership fee. Quarterly magazine published *In Trust.*

Registration	Date	Chassis	Body	New to	Fleet No	Status
CCK 663	1949	Leyland Titan PD2/3	Brush L27/26R	Ribble Motor Services	2687	A
DFV 146	1949	Leyland Titan PD2/5	Burlingham FH31/23C	Blackpool Corporation	246	A
760 CTD	1957	Leyland Titan PD2/20	Northern Counties H30/28R	Lytham St Annes Corporation	61	A
561 TD	1962	Daimler Fleetline CRG6LX	Northern Counties H43/33F	Lancashire United Transport	97	R
RRN 405	1962	Leyland Atlantean PDR1/1	Weymann L38/33F	Ribble Motor Services	1805	R
YFR 351	1962	Leyland Titan PD3/1	Metro Cammell FH41/32R	Blackpool Corporation	351	A
CTF 627B	1964	Leyland Titan PD2A/27	Massey H37/27F	Lytham St Annes Corporation	70	RP
HFR 512E	1967	Leyland Titan PD3A/1	Metro Cammell H41/30R	Blackpool Corporation	512	R
HFR 515E	1967	Leyland Titan PD3A/1	MCW H41/30R	Blackpool Corporation	515	A
PFR 554H	1970	AEC Swift MP2R	Marshall B47D	Blackpool Corporation	554	R
ATD 281J	1971	Leyland Atlantean PDR1/1	Northern Counties H44/33F	Lytham St Annes Corporation	77	R
RTJ 422L	1972	Daimler Fleetline CRG6LXB	Northern Counties H47/32F	Lancashire United Transport	394	A

Notes:
CTF 627B   On loan from St Helens Transport Museum

Restored last year by the Lancastrian Transport Trust, Lytham 70, a Massey-bodied Leyland PD2A/27 is seen here outside Lytham station, where the station building is now a public house. *Philip Lamb*

Legionnaire Group

Contact address: 66 Montfort Road, Strood, Rochester, Kent
ME2 3EX
E-mail: bob.wingrove@btinternet.com

Brief description: The group aims to restore at least one of each combination of chassis/Legionnaire so that Harrington's last body style is represented in preservation.

Registration	Date	Chassis	Body	New to	Fleet No	Status
72 MMJ	1964	Bedford VAL 14	Harrington C52F	Reliance Coaches, Meppershall	72	RP
CDK 409C	1965	Bedford VAL 14	Harrington C52F	Yelloway Motor Services, Rochdale		A
JNK 681C	1965	Ford Thames 36 676E	Harrington C52F	SP Coaches, Sutton		RP

Notes:
JNK 681C   Used as Harrington Demonstrator when new

Meltham Mills Bus Museum

Contact address: 1 Vicar Park Road, Norton Tower, Halifax
HX2 ONL
Brief description: A collection of privately-owned vehicles most of which operated originally in West Yorkshire.

Events planned: Please see enthusiast press for details.
Opening days/times: The collection is not normally open to the public, but an appointment to view can be arranged by contacting the above address.

Registration	Date	Chassis	Body	New to	Fleet No	Status
JUB 29	1932	Leyland Titan TD2	Eastern Counties L27/26R	Keighley-West Yorkshire Services	K451	A
JX 7046	1939	AEC Regent O661	Park Royal H30/26R	Halifax Corporation	80	A
JX 9106	1946	AEC Regal O662	Weymann	Hebble Motor Services	181	A
AJX 369	1946	AEC Regent III 9612E	Park Royal H33/26R	Halifax Joint Omnibus Committee	243	A
HHP 755	1948	Maudslay Regal III	Duple FC33F	Greenslades Tours, Exeter		A
JXN 370	1949	Leyland Titan 7RT	Park Royal H30/26RD	London Transport	RTL 47	A
BCP 671	1950	AEC Regent III 9612E	Park Royal H33/26R	Halifax Joint Omnibus Committee	277	R
LTF 254	1950	AEC Regent III 9612E	Park Royal H33/26R	Morecambe & Heysham Corporation	69	R
ROD 765	1958	AEC Regent V MD3RV	MCW H33/26RD	Devon General Omnibus & Touring Co	DR 765	R
3916 UB	1959	AEC Regent V 2D3RA	MCW H38/32R	Leeds City Transport	916	R
LJX 198	1959	AEC Regent V 2D3RA	MCW H39/32F	Hebble Motor Services	307	R
LJX 215	1960	AEC Regent V 2D3RA	MCW H40/32F	Halifax Joint Omnibus Committee	215	RP

Notes:

JUB 29	Rebodied in 1951 using 1932 body	HHP 755	Exhibited at the 1948 Commercial Motor Show
JX 9106	Converted to tow lorry in 1956 and renumbered L4	JXN 370	Originally H30/26R

Merseyside Transport Trust

Contact address: 88 Hawthorne Road, Bootle, Merseyside,
L20 9JX
E-mail: rob@aquaventurers.co.uk

Affiliation: NARTM; AEC Society; Leyland Society.
Brief description: A collection of around 35 vehicles, mostly from
the Merseyside area but including others of special interest.

Registration	Date	Chassis	Body	New to	Fleet No	Status
GKD 434	1946	AEC Regent II 0661	Weymann/LCPT H30/26R	Liverpool Corporation	A233	A
HKF 820	1949	AEC Regent III 9612E	Weymann/LCPT H30/26R	Liverpool Corporation	A344	RP
JKC 178	1949	Daimler CVA6	Northern Counties H30/26R	Liverpool Corporation	D553	A
KMN 519	1950	Leyland Comet CP01	Park Royal B30F	Douglas Corporation	21	R
LFM 756	1951	Bristol LL6B	ECW B39R	Crosville Motor Services	SLB175	R
MMN 302	1951	Leyland Olympic HR40	MCW B40F	Isle of Man Road Services	84	R
NMN 907	1951	Leyland Royal Tiger PSU1/13	Leyland B44F	Isle of Man Road Services	89	A
DWG 526	1951	Leyland Royal Tiger PSU1/15	Leyland C41C	W Alexander & Sons	PC30	RP
MKB 994	1952	AEC Regent III 9613A	Crossley H30/26R	Liverpool Corporation	A801	A
NKD 536	1953	AEC Regent III 9613S	Crossley H30/26R	Liverpool Corporation	A36	RP
NKD 540	1954	AEC Regent III 9613S	Saunders Roe H32/26R	Liverpool Corporation	A40	RP
RKC 262	1955	Leyland Titan PD2/20	Alexander H32/26R	Liverpool Corporation	L161	RP
SKB 168	1956	Leyland Royal Tiger PSU1/13	Crossley/MCW HDC23/21F	Liverpool Corporation	XL171	RP
SKB 224	1956	Leyland Titan PD2/20	Crossley/LCPT H32/26R	Liverpool Corporation	L227	RP
VKB 711	1956	Leyland Titan PD2/20	Crossley H33/29R	Liverpool Corporation	L255	RP
VKB 900	1957	AEC Regent V D3RV	MCW H33/29R	Liverpool Corporation	A267	R
VKB 841	1957	Leyland Titan PD2/20	Crossley H33/29R	Liverpool Corporation	L320	A
116 TMD	1959	AEC Bridgemaster B3RA	Park Royal H43/33R	Liverpool Corporation	E3	A
371 BKA	1959	AEC Regent V LD3RA	Park Royal FH40/32F	Liverpool Corporation	E1	R
372 BKA	1959	Leyland Atlantean PDR1/1	MCW H43/35F	Liverpool Corporation	E2	RP
256 SFM	1961	Bristol Lodekka FLF6B	ECW H38/22F	Crosville Motor Services	DFB43	A
875 VFM	1961	Bristol Lodekka FSF6G	ECW H34/26F	Crosville Motor Services	DFG65	RP
891 VFM	1961	Bristol Lodekka FSF6G	ECW O34/26F	Crosville Motor Services	DFG81	RP
501 KD	1962	Leyland Atlantean PDR1/1	MCW H43/35F	Liverpool Corporation	L501	R
GFM 180C	1965	Bristol Lodekka FS6B	ECW H33/27RD	Crosville Motor Services	DFB180	RP
FKF 801D	1966	Leyland Atlantean PDR1/1	MCW H43/35F	Liverpool City Transport	L801	A
FKF 835E	1967	Leyland Atlantean PDR1/1	MCW H43/28D	Liverpool City Transport	L835	RP
FKF 933G	1968	Leyland Panther PSUR1A/1R	MCW B47D	Liverpool City Transport	1054	RP
SKB 695G	1969	Bristol RELL6G	Park Royal B45D	Liverpool City Transport	2025	RP
UKA 562H	1969	Leyland Atlantean PDR2/1	Alexander H47/32D	Liverpool City Transport	1111	R
XKC 862K	1971	Leyland Atlantean PDR2/1	Alexander H49/31D	Merseyside PTE	1235	R
BKC 236K	1972	Leyland Atlantean PDR1A/1	Alexander H43/32F	Merseyside PTE	1236	R

Notes:

SKB 168   Originally B40D, numbered SL171; rebuilt by Metro
Cammell in 1961

116 TMD   Former AEC demonstrator; acquired by Liverpool
Corporation (E3) in 1959

891 VFM   Originally H34/26F

FKF 835E   Originally H43/35F. Rebuilt by Pennine Coachcraft
1969.

The Mike Sutcliffe Collection

Phone: Phone/Fax: 01525 221676
Affiliation: NARTM; Leyland Society member
Brief description: A collection of 20 vehicles, mainly buses of Leyland manufacture from the period 1908 to 1934, this is the most significant collection of of early motorbuses in the world, including the oldest British-built motorbus.

Opening days/times: Viewing can be arranged by prior appointment only. There is no charge, but donations are welcome.

Registration	Date	Chassis	Body	New to	Fleet No	Status
LN 7270	1908	Leyland X2	Thomas Tilling O18/16RO	London Central Motor Omnibus Co	14	R
HE 12	1913	Leyland S3.30.T	Brush B27F	Barnsley & District Electric Traction Co	5	RP
LF 9967	1913	Leyland S3.30.T	Birch O20/16RO	Wellingborough Motor Omnibus Co	H	R
CC 1087	1914	Leyland S4.36.T3	Leyland Ch32	London & North Western Railway	59	R
C 2367	1921	Leyland G2	Phoenix O23/20RO	Todmorden Corporation	14	R
BD 209	1921	Leyland G7	Dodson Ch/B32D	United Counties Omnibus Co	B15	R
DM 2583	1923	Leyland SG7	Leyland FB40D	Brookes Bros ('White Rose'), Rhyl	27	RP
XU 7498	1924	Leyland LB5	Dodson O26/22RO	Chocolate Express Omnibus Co	B6	R
BT 8939	1925	Leyland C7	Barnaby B26R	Lee & Beulah, Elloughton	17	RP
PW 8605	1926	ADC 415	United B35F	United Automobile Services	E61	A
VF 8157	1930	Chevrolet LQ	Bush & Twiddy C14D	Final, Hockwold		R
CK 4518	1931	Leyland Lion LT2	Leyland B30F	Ribble Motor Services	1161	A
YG 7831	1934	Leyland Tiger TS6	Northern Counties B36R	Todmorden Joint Omnibus Committee	15	A

Notes:

LF 9967	On loan to British Commercial Vehicle Museum, Leyland	BD 209	Formerly a Dodson demonstrator.
CC 1087	Re-registered XA8086 in 1919; reverted to CC1087 in 1980	VF 8157	Originally registered VF9126; acquired by Mulleys Motorways, Ixworth in 1940
C 2367	On loan to Manchester Museum of Transport	YG 7831	Rebuilt to recovery vehicle; to be restored as bus

North East Bus Preservation Society

Contact address: 'Relly Steading', Broom Park, Durham DH7 7RJ
Phone: 0191 384 5146
E-mail: r.l.kell@Durham.ac.uk
Affiliation: NARTM
Brief description: The collection is displayed at an 1820 former locomotive shed on the Bowes Railway. This accommodates up to 10 vehicles, and so vehicles rotate between this and other locations. If you wish to view a particular vehicle, you will need to mention this when making arrangements to view.

Opening days/times: Viewing by prior arrangement only.

Registration	Date	Chassis	Body	New to	Fleet No	Status
CN 4740	1931	SOS IM4	Short B34F	Northern General Transport	540	A
BTN 113	1934	Daimler COS4	Northern Coach Builders B34R	Newcastle Corporation	173	A
CN 6100	1934	Northern General Transport SE6 (LSE4)	Short B44F	Northern General Transport	604	RP
DPT 848	1939	Leyland Tiger TS8	Roe B32F	Sunderland District	159	R
EF 7380	1942	Leyland Titan TD7	Roe H26/22C	West Hartlepool Corporation	36	R
HHN 202	1947	Bristol L5G	ECW B35R	Bells, Westerhope		R
HUP 236	1948	Albion Valiant CX39N	ACB C33F	Economic, Whitburn	W7	R
JPT 544	1948	Daimler CVD6	Willowbrook B35F	Venture Transport Co, Consett	156	R
LVK 123	1948	Leyland Titan PD2/1	Leyland H30/26R	Newcastle Corporation	123	RP
CFK 340	1949	AEC Regal III 6821A	Burlingham C33F	Burnhams, Worcester		R
ABR 433	1949	Crossley DD42/7C	Crossley H56R	Sunderland Corporation	100	RP

Registration	Date	Chassis	Body	New to	Fleet No	Status
LPT 328	1950	AEC Regal III 9621E	Burlingham C33F	Gillet Bros	31	R
NVK 341	1950	AEC Regent III 9613A	Northern Coach Builders H30/26R	Newcastle Corporation	341	R
SHN 301	1952	AEC Regal IV 9821E	Burlingham C41C	Scotts Greys, Darlington	5	R
CBR 539	1952	Guy Arab III	Roe H33/25R	Sunderland Corporation	139	RP
PHN 699	1952	Guy Arab III	Roe B41C	Darlington Corporation	26	RP
DCN 83	1953	AEC Beadle	Beadle C35F	Northern General Transport	1483	A
SPT 65	1955	Guy Arab LUF	Weymann B44F	Northern General Transport	1665	RP
TUP 859	1956	AEC Regent V MD3RV	Roe H35/28R	Hartlepool Corporation	4	RP
UFJ 292	1957	Guy Arab IV	Massey H30/26R	Exeter Corporation	52	R
VUP 328	1957	Leyland Tiger Cub PSUC1/1	Crossley B44F	Economic, Whitburn	A2	A
MJD 759	1958	AEC Reliance MU3RV	Roe C41C	Essex County Coaches, Stratford		R
YPT 796	1958	AEC Reliance MU3RV	Roe C41C	Economic, Whitburn	W3	R
AFT 930	1958	Leyland Titan PD3/4	MCCW H41/32R	Tynemouth & District	230	RP
WNL 259A	1962	AEC Reliance 4MU3R	Plaxton B55F	Economic, Whitburn	W5	R
221 JVK	1962	Leyland Atlantean PDR1/1	Alexander H44/34F	Newcastle Corporation	221	RP
ACU 304B	1963	Leyland Leopard PSU3/3R	Plaxton B55F	Stanhope Motor Services		R
6249 UP	1963	Leyland Leopard PSU3/3RT	Alexander DP51F	Venture Transport Co, Consett	249	R
EUP 405B	1964	AEC Routemaster 3R2RH	Park Royal H41/31F	Northern General Transport	2105	R
PCN 762	1964	AEC Routemaster 3R2RH	Park Royal H41/31F	Northern General Transport	2099	R
WBR 248	1964	Atkinson Alpha PM746HL	Marshall B45D	Sunderland Corporation	48	R
FBR 53D	1966	Leyland Panther PSUR1/1R	Strachan B47D	Sunderland Corporation	53	R
ECU 201E	1967	Bristol RESL6L	ECW B45D	South Shields Corporation	1	R
WHN 411G	1969	Bristol VRTSL6LX	ECW H39/31F	United Automobile Services	601	A
PCW 203J	1971	Bristol RESL6L	Pennine B45F	Burnley Colne & Nelson Joint Committee	103	R
MCN 30K	1972	Leyland/NGT Tynesider	MCCW/Northern General H39/29F	Northern General Transport	3000	R
GGR 103N	1974	Leyland Atlantean AN68/2R	Northern Counties H47/36F	OK Motor Services		RP
GUP 907N	1975	Bristol LH6L	ECW B43F	United Automobile Services	1623	R
TUP 329R	1976	Bristol VRTSL3/501	ECW H43/31F	Northern General Transport	3329	RP
VPT 598R	1977	Leyland National 11351A/1R	Leyland National B49F	Northern General Transport Co	4598	RP
RCU 838S	1978	Leyland Fleetline FE30AGR	Alexander H44/30F	Tyne & Wear PTE	838	R
UTN 501Y	1983	MCW Metrobus DR102/31	MCW H46/31F	Northern General Transport Co	3501	R

Notes:

HHN 202	Rebodied 1957 with 1946 body; passed to Durham District Services (DB216) in 1959
ABR 433	Fitted with Gardner 5LW engine
WNL 259A	Originally registered 8031PT
ACU 304B	Originally registered 6MPT
PCN 762	Originally registered RCN699
MCN 30K	Rebuilt from 1958 Leyland Titan PD3/4 new to Tyneside Tramways & Tramroads Co (49) registered NNL 49
RCU 838S	Originally H44/27D

Back on the road again in 2000 was Newcastle 341, a Northern Coach Builders-bodied AEC Regent III new in 1950, and today part of the North East Bus Museum collection. *Philip Lamb*

Apart from London Transport and British European Airways, only Northern General bought AEC Routemasters new. This is Northern General 2105, and also a North East Bus Museum vehicle. *Philip Lamb*

Ribble Vehicle Preservation Trust

Contact address: 6 Crompton Road, Lostock, Bolton BL6 4LP
Brief description: The Trust promotes the preservation and restoration of vehicles from Ribble and associated companies.

Registration	Date	Chassis	Body	New to	Fleet No	Status
RN 7588	1935	Leyland Tiger TS7	Burlingham B35F	Ribble Motor Services	209	R
ACK 796	1944	Guy Arab II	Northern Counties / Bond UL27/26R	Ribble Motor Services	2413	A
CRG 811	1947	Daimler CVD6	Alexander C35F	Aberdeen Corporation	11	A
ACB 904	1947	Guy Arab II	Northern Counties	Blackburn Corporation	502	A
CRS 834	1948	Daimler CVD6	Walker / Aberdeen CT C31F	Aberdeen Corporation	44	A
CCK 359	1948	Leyland Titan PD2/3	Leyland L27/26R	Ribble Motor Services	2584	A
MTC 540	1950	AEC Regent III 9613E	Park Royal H30/26R	Morecambe & Heysham Corporation	72	RP
DRN 289	1950	Leyland Titan PD2/3	Leyland L27/26RD	Ribble Motor Services	1349	A
DCK 219	1951	Leyland Titan PD2/3	East Lancashire Coachbuilders FCL27/22RD	Ribble Motor Services	1248	RP
ERN 700	1952	Leyland Royal Tiger PSU1/13	Leyland B44F	Ribble Motor Services	377	A
FCK 844	1954	Leyland Tiger Cub PSUC1/1	Saunders Roe B44F	Ribble Motor Services	412	R
FCK 884	1954	Leyland Tiger Cub PSUC1/1T	Saunders Roe B44F	Ribble Motor Services	452	R
HRN 39	1955	Leyland Titan PD2/13	Metro Cammell H33/28RD	Ribble Motor Services	1399	A
JRN 41	1956	Leyland Tiger Cub PSUC1/2T	Burlingham C41F	Ribble Motor Services	975	RP
JCK 530	1956	Leyland Titan PD2/12	Burlingham H33/28RD	Ribble Motor Services	1455	R
JCK 542	1956	Leyland Titan PD2/12	Burlingham H33/28RD	Ribble Motor Services	1467	RP
528 CTF	1957	Leyland Titan PD2/40	Weymann L29/28RD	J Fishwick & Sons, Leyland	5	R
881 BTF	1958	Leyland Titan PD2/41	East Lancashire Coachbuilders H35/28R	Lancaster City Transport	881	A
KCK 869	1958	Leyland Titan PD3/4	Burlingham FH41/31F	Ribble Motor Services	1523	A
KCK 914	1958	Leyland Titan PD3/4	Burlingham FH41/31F	Ribble Motor Services	1553	A
NRN 586	1960	Leyland Atlantean PDR1/1	Metro Cammell H44/33F	Ribble Motor Services	1686	R
SFV 421	1960	Leyland Atlantean PDR1/1	Weymann CH34/16Ft	W C Standerwick	25	A
PRN 145	1961	Leyland Atlantean PDR1/1	Metro Cammell H44/33F	Scout Motor Services, Preston	5	RP
PRN 906	1961	Leyland Titan PD3/4	Metro Cammell H39/31F	Preston Corporation	14	RP
RRN 428	1962	Leyland Atlantean PDR1/1	Weymann CH39/20F	Ribble Motor Services	1279	RP
TCK 465	1963	Leyland Leopard PSU3/1R	Marshall B53F	Ribble Motor Services	465	RP
TCK 726	1963	Leyland Leopard PSU3/3RT	Harrington C49F	Ribble Motor Services	726	RP
ARN 811C	1965	Leyland Leopard PSU3/3RT	Weymann DP49F	Ribble Motor Services	811	RP
HRN 249G	1969	Bristol RELL6G	ECW B41D	Ribble Motor Services	249	RP
FPT 6G	1969	Leyland Leopard PSU3/3RT	Plaxton C51F	Weardale Motor Services, Frosterley		A
LRN 321J	1970	Bristol RESL6L	Marshall B47F	Ribble Motor Services	321	A
NCK 338J	1971	Bristol RESL6L	ECW B47F	Ribble Motor Services	338	RP
PRN 79K	1972	Bristol VRLLH6L	ECW CH42/18Ct	W C Standerwick	S79	RP
NNC 855P	1976	AEC Reliance 6U3ZR	Duple C49F	Yelloway Motor Services, Rochdale		R
MFR 306P	1976	Leyland Leopard PSU3C/2R	Alexander B53F	Lancaster City Transport	306	R
XCW 955R	1978	Leyland National 11351A/1R	Leyland National B49F	Fishwick of Leyland	24	RP

Notes:

RN 7588	Rebodied 1949	DCK 219	White Lady double deck coach
CRG 811	Rebodied 1958	ERN 700	Originally B44F
ACB 904	Breakdown Vehicle	SFV 421	Gay Hostess double deck motorway coach
CRS 834	Body rebuilt 1962	FPT 6G	Eaton 2-speed axle

Another recent restoration is Ribble 1455, a 1956 Leyland PD2/12 with high-bridge bodywork by Burlingham of Blackpool.
Philip Lamb

RTW Bus Group

Contact address: 7 Oldbury Close , St Mary Cray ,BR5 3TH
Affiliation: RT/RF Register, Cobham Bus Museum, HCVS
Brief description: The group was formed in 1999 and comprises

the owners of the preserved RTW vegicles and those interested in the type. The vehicles appear at rallies from time to time. A video on the history of the RTW is available from the group.

Registration	Date	Chassis	Body	New to	Fleet No	Status
KGK 529	1949	Leyland Titan 6RT	Leyland H30/26R	London Transport	RTW 29	R
KGK 575	1949	Leyland Titan 6RT	Leyland H30/26R	London Transport	RTW 75	RP
KLB 908	1949	Leyland Titan 6RT	Leyland H30/26RD	London Transport	RTW 178	R
KLB 915	1949	Leyland Titan 6RT	Leyland H30/26R	London Transport	RTW 185	R
LLU 957	1950	Leyland Titan 6RT	Leyland H30/26R	London Transport	RTW 467	R
LLU 987	1950	Leyland Titan 6RT	Leyland H30/26R	London Transport	RTW 497	R

SELNEC Preservation Society

Contact address: 16 Thurleigh Road, Didsbury, Manchester M20 2DF
Brief description: A collection of buses from the SELNEC era including SELNEC Standards, the trail-blazing 'Mancunian' and other vehicles from the Greater Manchester area.
Events planned: The operational vehicles will appear at a range of local rallies and shows.

Registration	Date	Chassis	Body	New to	Fleet No	Status
EN 9965	1950	Leyland Titan PD2/4	Weymann -	Bury Corporation	165	RP
DNF 708C	1965	Daimler Fleetline CRG6LX	Metro Cammell O43/29C	Manchester Corporation	4708	A
END 832D	1966	Leyland Atlantean PDR1/2	Metro Cammell H43/32F	Manchester Corporation	3832	RP
LNA 166G	1968	Leyland Atlantean PDR2/1	Park Royal H26/7D	Manchester Corporation	1066	R
NNB 547H	1969	Leyland Atlantean PDR2/1	East Lancashire Coachbuilders H47/32F	Manchester Corporation	1142	A
NNB 589H	1970	Daimler Fleetline CRG6LXB	Park Royal H47/28D	Manchester Corporation	2130	A
ONF 865H	1970	Leyland Atlantean PDR2/1	Park Royal H47/28D	SELNEC PTE	1177	A
RNA 220J	1971	Daimler Fleetline CRG6LXB	Park Royal H47/29D	SELNEC PTE	2220	A
PNF 941J	1971	Leyland Atlantean PDR1A/1	Northern Counties H43/32F	SELNEC PTE	EX1	R
TNB 759K	1972	Daimler Fleetline CRG6LXB	Northern Counties H45/27D	SELNEC PTE	EX19	A
VNB 177L	1972	Daimler Fleetline CRG6LXB	Northern Counties H45/27D	SELNEC PTE	7206	R
VNB 203L	1972	Daimler Fleetline CRG6LXB	Northern Counties H31/4D	SELNEC PTE	7232	R
YDB 453L	1972	Seddon Pennine IV-236	Seddon DP25F	SELNEC PTE	1700	RP
AJA 408L	1973	Bristol VRTSL2/6LX	ECW H43/32F	SELNEC Cheshire Bus Co	408	RP
WWH 43L	1973	Daimler Fleetline CRG6LXB	Park Royal H43/32F	SELNEC PTE	7185	R
XJA 534L	1973	Leyland Atlantean AN68/1R	Park Royal H43/32F	SELNEC PTE	7143	A
XVU 341M	1973	Seddon Pennine IV-236	Seddon B23F	SELNEC PTE	1711	A
BNE 764N	1974	Bristol LH6L	ECW B43F	Greater Manchester PTE	1321	A
BNE 751N	1974	Leyland Atlantean AN68/1R	Northern Counties H43/32F	Greater Manchester PTE	7501	A
BNE 729N	1974	Seddon Pennine IV-236	Seddon B19F+19	Greater Manchester PTE	1735	A
XVU 363M	1974	Seddon Pennine IV-236	Seddon B19F+19	Greater Manchester PTE	1733	A
HNB 24N	1975	Leyland National 10351/1R	Leyland National B41F	Greater Manchester Transport	105	RP
OBN 502R	1977	Leyland Fleetline FE30GR	Northern Counties H43/32F	Lancashire United Transport	6901	A
XBU 1S	1978	Leyland Fleetline FE30GR	Northern Counties H43/32F	Greater Manchester PTE	8001	R
BNC 960T	1979	Leyland Atlantean AN68A/1R	Park Royal H43/32F	Greater Manchester PTE	7960	A
GBU 1V	1979	MCW Metrobus DR101/6	Metro Cammell H43/30F	Greater Manchester PTE	5001	RP
NJA 568W	1980	Bristol Olympian B45	Northern Counties H43/30F	Greater Manchester Transport	1451	RP
GNF 15V	1980	Leyland Titan TNTL11/1RF	Park Royal H47/26F	Greater Manchester PTE	4015	A
DWH 706W	1981	Leyland Fleetline FE30GR	Northern Counties H43/32F	Lancashire United Transport	6990	R
A765 NNA	1984	Leyland Atlantean AN68D/1R	Northern Counties H43/32F	Greater Manchester Transport	8765	RP
C751 YBA	1985	Dennis Domino SDA 1201	Northern Counties B24F	Greater Manchester PTE	1751	R

Notes:

EN 9965 — Converted to Breakdown Vehicle
DNF 708C — Originally H43/32F; awaiting repatriation from USA
LNA 166G — Originally H47/29D; converted by Greater Manchester PTE for use as 'Exhibus' exhibition vehicle - restored in this condition
PNF 941J — Exhibited at 1970 Commercial Motor Show as prototype SELNEC Standard
VNB 203L — Originally H45/27D. Used as exhibition vehice.
VNB 177L — Exhibited at 1972 Commercial Motor Show
OBN 502R — Passed to Greater Manchester PTE (6901) in 1981

XBU 1S — First GMT Leyand Fleetline Standard
BNC 960T — Last Park Royal Bodied Standard
GBU 1V — GM First Metrobus
NJA 568W — Exhibited at 1980 Commercial Motor Show. GM First Olympian
GNF 15V — GM Last Titan
DWH 706W — Passed to Greater Manchester PTE (6990) in 1981. GM Last Fleetline
C751 YBA — Exhibited at 1984 Commercial Motor Show

Solent Transport Trust

Contact address: 'Paynter', Hook Lane, Hook-by-Warsash, Southampton SO31 9HH
Affiliation: NARTM; WOMP

Brief description: The collection includes a selection of Southampton's fleet from the early 1970s. The small membership carries out restoration work.

Registration	Date	Chassis	Body	New to	Fleet No	Status
JOW 928	1955	Guy Arab UF	Park Royal B39F	Southampton Corporation	255	A
318 AOW	1962	AEC Regent V 2D3RA	Park Royal H37/29R	Southampton Corporation	318	A
335 AOW	1963	Leyland Titan PD2A/27	Park Royal H37/29R	Southampton Corporation	335	A
BTR 361B	1964	AEC Regent V 2D3RA	Neepsend H37/29R	Southampton Corporation	361	R
KOW 910F	1967	AEC Regent V 3D2RA	Neepsend H40/30R	Southampton Corporation	402	A
JOW 499E	1967	AEC Swift MP2R	Strachan B47D	Southampton Corporation	1	A
GTP 175F	1967	Leyland Panther Cub	MCW B42D	City of Portsmouth	175	R
PCG 889G	1968	AEC Reliance 6MU3R	Plaxton C45F	Coliseum Coaches, Southampton		A
PCG 888G	1968	AEC Reliance 6U3ZR	Plaxton C55F	Coliseum Coaches, Southampton		A
TTA 400H	1970	Bedford SB5	Duple C41F	Otter Coaches, Ottery St Mary, Devon		A
BCR 379K	1972	Seddon Pennine RU	Pennine B44F	Southampton Corporation	15	R

Notes:

JOW 928	Originally B36D
BTR 361B	On display at CPPTD Museum, Portsmouth
PCG 888G	Originally C57F

Southdown Historic Vehicle Group

Contact address: 92 Lyndhurst Road, Worthing West Sussex
E-mail: pd3@btinternet.com
Website: http:/home.fastnet.co.uk/gerrycork/worthingbusrally.htm
Brief description: A private collection of vehicles most of which operated for Southdown Motor Services or which have south coast connections. The collection is not on public view but vehicles are rallied and often appear in service at running days.

Events planned: 29 July 2001 — Worthing Bus Rally & Running Day.

Registration	Date	Chassis	Body	New to	Fleet No	Status
EHO 869	1943	Guy Arab II	Reading CO30/26R	Gosport & Fareham Omnibus Co	57	RP
XUF 141	1960	Leyland Tiger Cub PSUC1/2	Weymann C41F	Southdown Motor Services	1141	R
70 AUF	1962	Commer Avenger IV	Harrington C—F	Southdown Motor Services	70	A
WTS 429A	1962	Commer Avenger IV	Harrington C35C	Southdown Motor Services	60	
972 CUF	1964	Leyland Titan PD3/4	Northern Counties FH39/30F	Southdown Motor Services	972	RP
DRR 153B	1964	Leyland Titan PD3/4	Northern Counties FHO39/30F	Southdown Motor Services	419	R
PRX 190B	1964	Leyland Titan PD3/4	Northern Counties FHO39/30F	Southdown Motor Services	416	R
PRX 200B	1964	Leyland Titan PD3/4	Northern Counties FHO39/30F	Southdown Motor Services	418	R
ZV 1465	1964	Leyland Titan PD3/4	Northern Counties FHO39/30F	Southdown Motor Services	415	RP
BUF 260C	1965	Leyland Titan PD3/4	Northern Counties FH39/30F	Southdown Motor Services	260	R
BUF 277C	1965	Leyland Titan PD3/4	Northern Counties FH39/30F	Southdown Motor Services	277	R
BUF 426C	1965	Leyland Titan PD3/4	Northern Counties FCO39/30F	Southdown Motor Services	426	R
CJN 436C	1965	Leyland Titan PD3/6	Massey H38/32R	Southend Corporation	336	
FCD 292D	1966	Leyland Titan PD3/4	Northern Counties FH-/-F	Southdown Motor Services	292	RP

Registration	Date	Chassis	Body	New to	Fleet No	Status
FCD 294D	1966	Leyland Titan PD3/4	Northern Counties FH39/30F	Southdown Motor Services	294	R
FCD 307D	1966	Leyland Titan PD3/4	Northern Counties FH-/-F	Southdown Motor Services	307	RP
LFS 296F	1968	Bristol VRTLL6G	ECW	Eastern Scottish	544	RP
KUF 199F	1968	Leyland Leopard PSU3/1RT	Willowbrook B45F	Southdown Motor Services	199	R
SYX 569F	1968	Leyland Leopard PSU4/4R	Duple C41F	Grey Green (G Ewer) London		A
PUF 165H	1969	Leyland Leopard PSU3/1RT	Northern Counties DP49F	Southdown Motor Services	465	RP
TCD 490J	1970	Bristol RESL6L	Marshall B45F	Southdown Motor Services	490	RP
TCD 374J	1970	Daimler Fleetline CRG6LX	Northern Counties	Southdown Motor Services	374	RP
TCD 383J	1970	Daimler Fleetline CRG6LX	Northern Counties	Southdown Motor Services	383	RP
UUF 516J	1971	Bristol VRTSL6G	ECW H-/-F	Southdown Motor Services	516	RP
SCD 731N	1974	Leyland Atlantean AN68/1R	Park Royal - Roe H43/30F	Southdown Motor Services	731	R
RUF 37R	1977	Leyland National 11351A/2R	Leyland National B44D	Southdown Motor Services	37	RP

Notes:

EHO 869	Rebodied in 1953	ZV 1465	Originally registered 415 DCD
WTS 429A	Originally registered 60 AUF	PRX 200B	Originally registered 418 DCD
DRR 153B	Originally registered 419 DCD	PRX 190B	Originally registered 416 DCD

Seen at Pool Valley, Brighton,is Southdown 199, a Willowbrook-bodied Leyland Leopard BET-style saloon from the Southdown Historic Vehicle Group collection. *Philip Lamb*

Telford Bus Group

Contact address: 47 Ian Road, Newchapel, Stoke-on-Trent, Staffs ST7 4PP

Brief description: The Telford Bus Group has a collection of privately-owned buses and coaches in various parts of England. The Group has become known for its Bedford VALs of which 12 examples are preserved, with examples of several body types. Other vehicles include Daimler Fleetline 'Mancunian', Seddon Pennine VI, Commer Avenger and Leyland Leopard 'Midland Red S27 type'. Not all vehicles are restored and some are long term projects.

Registration	Date	Chassis	Body	New to	Fleet No	Status
386 DD	1961	Bedford J2	Plaxton C20F	Talbott, Moreton-in-Marsh		RP
3190 UN	1962	Commer Avenger IV	Plaxton C41F	Wright, Penycae		RP
9797 DP	1964	Bedford VAL 14	Duple C52F	Smiths, Reading		RP
EHL 472D	1966	Bedford VAL 14	Plaxton C52F	West Riding Automobile Co	3	R
UWX 981F	1968	Bedford VAL 70	Plaxton C52F			RP
RCB 345G	1969	Bedford VAL 70	Duple C52F	Cook, Dunstable		RP
WWY 115G	1969	Bedford VAL 70	Plaxton C53F	Abbey Coachways, Selby		R
FYG 663J	1970	Bedford VAL 70	Willowbrook B56F	Wigmore, Dinnington		RP
VBD 310H	1970	Bedford VAL 70	Plaxton C48F	Coales, Woolaston		R
YYB 239H	1970	Bedford VAL 70	Caetano C53F	Clevedon Motorways, Clevedon		A
BHO 670J	1971	Bedford VAL 70	Duple C53F	Castle Coaches, Waterlooville		R
RAR 690J	1971	Bedford VAL 70	Van Hool C51F	All Seasons, London		R
RNA 236J	1971	Daimler Fleetline CRG6LXB	Park Royal H47/29D	SELNEC PTE	2236	R
FAR 724K	1972	Bedford VAL 70	Duple C53F	Langley Coaches, Slough		R
CDC 166K	1972	Seddon Pennine VI	Plaxton C45F	Bob's, Middlesborough	26	RP
CDC 168K	1972	Seddon Pennine VI	Plaxton C41F	Bob's, Middlesborough	28	R
ANO 395L	1973	Bedford VAL 70	Plaxton C53F	Golden Boy Coaches		A
JHA 227L	1973	Leyland Leopard PSU3B/2R	Marshall DP49F	Midland Red Omnibus Co	227	RP

Notes:

RNA 236J   Mancunian
ANO 395L   Caravan conversion

Many Telford Bus Group vehicles, are, like this Duple Vega Major-bodied Bedford VAL14, privately owned. The VAL was new to Smiths of Reading in 1964. *Philip Lamb*

Three Counties Bus and Commercial Vehicle Museum

Contact address: 83 Millwright Way, Flitwick, Beds MK45 1BQ
Phone: 01525 370578 or 01525 712091
Web site: www. ampyx.org.uk/three_c
Affiliation: NARTM
Brief description: Established to provide a focus for bus

preservation in Bedfordshire, Buckinghamshire and Hertfordshire. Seeks to ensure a long-term future for the vehicles and secure permanent undercover accommodation.
Events planned: Please see enthusiast press for planned Operating Days.

Registration	Date	Chassis	Body	New to	Fleet No	Status
BXD 628	1935	Leyland Cub KPO3	Short B20F	London Transport	C4	RP
FXT 122	1939	Leyland Cub REC	LPTB B20F	London Transport	CR16	RP
MXX 434	1952	AEC Regal IV 9821LT RF	Metro Cammell B39F	London Transport	RF 457	R
LYR 915	1952	AEC Regent III O961 RT	Weymann H30/26R	London Transport	RT 3496	R
MXX 332	1952	Guy Special NLLVP	ECW B26F	London Transport	GS 32	R
MXX 489	1953	AEC Regal IV 9821LT RF	Metro Cammell B39F	London Transport	RF 512	RP
OVL 473	1960	Bristol Lodekka FS5G	ECW H33/27RD	Lincolnshire Road Car Co	2378	R
KBD 712D	1966	Bristol Lodekka FS6G	ECW H33/27RD	United Counties Omnibus Co	712	R
DEK 3D	1966	Leyland Titan PD2/37	Massey H37/27F	Wigan Corporation	140	R
UXD 129G	1968	Bristol RELL6L	ECW B48D	Luton Corporation Transport	129	RP
NPD 127L	1973	Leyland National 1151/1R/0402	Leyland National B49F	London Country Bus Services	LNC27	A
SOA 674S	1977	Leyland Leopard PSU3E/4R	Plaxton C49F	Midland Red Omnibus Co	674	R

Right: Many Three Counties Bus and Commercial Vehicle Museum buses are, like RT3496 seen here in Luton, of London Transport origin. A Weymann-bodied AEC Regent III, it was new in 1952. *Philip Lamb*

Wealdstone & District Vintage Vehicle Collection

Contact address: 91 Graham Road, Wealdstone, Middx HA3 5RE
E-mail: oldbusgarage@sftt.co.uk
Web site: www.sftt.co.uk/busgarage
Brief description: A small collection of mainly London buses from

the 1950s. Examples of which regularly attend rallies. Anyone wishing to visit or assist with the vehicles is welcome. Please write to the address given.

Registration	Date	Chassis	Body	New to	Fleet No	Status
DL 9706	1935	Dennis Lancet	ECW B36R	Southern Vectis Omnibus Co	516	A
KLB 716	1950	AEC Regent III O961 RT	Park Royal H30/26R	London Transport	RT 1594	R
KYY 622	1950	AEC Regent III O961 RT	Park Royal H30/26R	London Transport	RT 1784	R
MLL 817	1952	AEC Regal IV 9821LT RF	Metro Cammell B37F	London Transport	RF 280	R
MXX 410	1953	AEC Regal IV 9821LT RF	Metro Cammell B41F	London Transport	RF 433	R
MXX 430	1953	AEC Regal IV 9821LT RF	Metro Cammell B39F	London Transport	RF 453	R
NLE 939	1953	AEC Regent III O961 RT	Park Royal H30/26R	London Transport	RT 4275	RP

Notes:
DL 9706   Rebodied 1944

Right: Another collection based largely on former London Transport buses is the Wealdstone & District Vintage Vehicle Collection. This is its RF280, taking part in an RF Running Day at Stoke D'Abernon station in October 1997. *Philip Lamb*

The West Country Historic Omnibus & Transport Trust

Contact address: The Secretary, 13 Dokkum Road, Crediton, Devon EX17 3DJ
Affiliation: NARTM
Brief description: It is hoped to stage an event in the summer/autumn at a West Country location. Taking the form of a commercial vehicle rally, it will include heritage bus rides using vehicles of local origin/interest.

Registration	Date	Chassis	Body	New to	Fleet No	Status
TUO 217J	1970	Leyland Panther PSUR1B/1R	Marshall B—D	Devon General Omnibus & Touring Co	217	R
A927 MDV	1983	Ford Transit 1 160	Carlyle B16F	Devon General Ltd	7	R

Notes:
TUO 217J — Ordered by Exeter City Transport. Converted to publicity vehicle in 1980.

West Midlands Bus Preservation Society

Contact address: Secretary, 5 Pommel Close, Walsall WS5 4QE
Brief description: The main core of the collection is of vehicles from the West Midlands PTE in the period 1969 to 1986. Other artefacts are being collected for inclusion in a planned transport museum.
Opening days/times: Vehicles can be viewed by special arrangement.

Registration	Date	Chassis	Body	New to	Fleet No	Status
VG 5541	1933	Bristol GJW	Weymann O28/26R	Norwich Electric Tramways		A
GKE 68	1939	Bristol K5G	Weymann H28/26R	Chatham & District Traction Co	874	A
DUK 278	1946	Guy Arab II	Roe H31/25R	Wolverhampton Corporation	378	RP
KHA 301	1948	BMMO C1	Duple C30C	BMMO ('Midland Red')	3301	R
GOU 732	1949	Tilling Stevens K6LA7	Scottish Aviation C33F	Altonian Coaches, Alton		R
LTA 813	1950	Bristol KS5G	ECW L27/28R	Western National Omnibus Co	994	R
OTT 43	1953	Bristol LS6G	ECW C39F	Western National Omnibus Co (Royal Blue)	2200	R
UHY 362	1955	Bristol KSW6B	ECW H32/28R	Bristol Tramways & Carriage Co	8322	R
56 GUO	1961	Bristol MW6G	ECW C39F	Western National Omnibus Co (Royal Blue)	2267	RP
ARN 658C	1965	Leyland Titan PD3A/1	MCW H39/31F	Preston Corporation	73	A
EHA 424D	1966	BMMO D9	Willowbrook-BMMO H40/32RD	BMMO ('Midland Red')	5424	R
OTA 640G	1969	Bristol RELH6G	ECW C45F	Southern National Omnibus Co (Royal Blue)	2380	R
NOV 880G	1969	Daimler Fleetline CRG6LX	Park Royal H43/29D	Birmingham City Transport	3880	RP
SOE 913H	1969	Daimler Fleetline CRG6LX-33	Park Royal H47/33D	West Midlands PTE	3913	A
TOB 997H	1970	Daimler Fleetline CRG6LX-33	Park Royal H47/33D	West Midlands PTE	3997	RP
YOX 133K	1971	Daimler Fleetline CRG6LX	Park Royal H43/33F	West Midlands PTE	4133	A
NOB 413M	1974	Bristol VRTSL6LX	MCW H43/33F	West Midlands PTE	4413	A
NOC 600R	1976	Leyland Fleetline FE30AGR	Park Royal H43/33F	West Midlands PTE	6600	A

Registration	Date	Chassis	Body	New to	Fleet No	Status
SDA 757S	1977	Leyland Fleetline FE30AGR	East Lancashire Coachbuilders H43/33F	West Midlands PTE	6757	A
WDA 835T	1978	MCW Metrobus DR102/1	MCW H43/30F	West Midlands PTE	6835	RP
WDA 956T	1979	Leyland Fleetline FE30AGR	MCW B37F	West Midlands PTE	1956	A
WDA 986T	1979	Leyland Fleetline FE30AGR	MCW H43/33F	West Midlands PTE	6986	R
AOL 17T	1979	Leyland National 11351/1A/1R	Leyland National B36D	West Midlands PTE	1017	A
GOG 214W	1981	MCW Metrobus DR102/18	MCW H43/30F	West Midlands PTE	2214	A

Notes:

VG 5541	Converted to Diesel 1938, Open top 1950
DUK 278	Rebodied 1952
ARN 658C	No staircase - converted to driver training vehicle by West Midlands PTE (8658)
TOB 997H	Gardner 6LXB engine fitted after acquisition by C J Partridge & Son, Hadleigh
WDA 835T	Exhibited at 1978 Commercial Motor Show
WDA 956T	Originally double deck bus (H43/33F) 6956; rebuilt as single-decker in 1994
AOL 17T	Originally B50F

BMMO C1 with Duple coachwork, No 3301 was completed in 1948. After a long career with Midland Red, it passed into the care of the 3301 Group, and is currently part of the West Midlands Bus Preservation Society collection. *Philip Lamb*

West of England Transport Collection

Contact address: 15 Land Park, Chulmleigh, Devon, EX18 7BH
Affiliation: NARTM
Brief description: A large private collection of vehicles, mainly from West Country major operators. The collection includes buses, coach-es and transport memorabilia.

Events planned: 7 October 2001 — Annual WETC Open Day.
Opening days/times: Viewing at other times by prior arrangement with C. T. Shears, tel: 01769 580811.

Registration	Date	Chassis	Body	New to	Fleet No	Status
UO 2331	1927	Austin 20 5PL	Tiverton B13F	Sidmouth Motor Co		RP
VW 203	1927	Leyland Lion PLSC3	Mumford B—R	National Omnibus & Transport Co	2407	A
JY 124	1932	Tilling Stevens B10 A2 Express	Beadle B—R	Western National Omnibus Co		A
OD 5868	1933	Leyland Lion LT5	Weymann B31F	Devon General Omnibus & Touring Co	68	A
OD 7500	1934	AEC Regent O661	Brush H30/26R	Devon General Omnibus & T Touring Co	DR213	R
ATT 922	1935	Bristol JJW6A	Beadle B35R	Western National Omnibus Co		RP
ADV 128	1935	Bristol JO5G	Beadle B—R	Western National Omnibus Co		A
AUO 74	1935	Leyland Lion LT5A	(chassis only)	Devon General Omnibus & Touring Co	SL79	A
BTF 25	1936	Leyland Titan TD4c	Leyland FH30/24R	Lytham St Annes Corporation	45	A
ETT 995	1938	AEC Regal I O661 rebuild	Saunders Roe H30/26R	Devon General Omnibus & Touring Co	DR705	A
BOW 169	1938	Bristol L5G		Hants & Dorset Motor Services	TS676	A
EFJ 666	1938	Leyland Tiger TS8	Cravens B32R	Exeter Corporation	66	R
EFJ 241	1938	Leyland Titan TD5	Leyland H30/26R	Exeter Corporation	26	A
EUF 204	1938	Leyland Titan TD5	Park Royal H28/26R	Southdown Motor Services	204	A
DOD 474	1940	AEC Regal I O662	Weymann B35F	Devon General Omnibus & Touring Co	SR474	A
FTA 634	1941	Bristol K5G	ECW L27/28R	Western National Omnibus Co	345	RP
GTA 395	1941	Bristol LL5G	Brislington Body Works B39R	Southern National Omnibus Co	373	RP
JTA 314	1943	Guy Arab II	Roe H31/25RD	Devon General Omnibus & Touring Co	DG314	A
DJY 965	1948	Crossley DD42/5	Crossley L27/26R	Plymouth Corporation	335	RP
GLJ 957	1948	Leyland Titan PD1A	ECW L27/26R	Hants & Dorset Motor Services	PD959	A
MAF 544	1949	Austin CXB	Mann Egerton FC31C	J J Pollard, Hayle		RP
KUO 972	1949	Bristol K6B	ECW L27/28R	Western National Omnibus Co	959	A
JFJ 606	1949	Daimler CVD6	Brush H30/26R	Exeter Corporation	43	A
LUO 595	1950	AEC Regal III 6821A	Weymann B35F	Devon General Omnibus & Touring Co	SR 595	RP
HJY 296	1953	Leyland Titan PD2/1	Leyland H30/26R	Plymouth Corporation	396	A
TFJ 808	1956	Guy Arab IV	Massey H30/26R	Exeter Corporation	50	A
OCO 502	1958	Leyland Titan PD2/40	MCW H30/26R	Plymouth Corporation	102	R
974 AFJ	1960	Guy Arab IV	Massey H31/26R	Exeter Corporation	74	R
1 RDV	1964	AEC Reliance 2MU3RA	Harrington C41F	Devon General Grey Cars	1	R
CTT 513C	1965	AEC Regent V 2D3RA	Park Royal H40/29F	Devon General Omnibus & Touring Co	513	R
GNM 235N	1975	Bristol LHL6L	Plaxton C51F	Caroline Seagull, Great Yarmouth		R
CRM 927T	1979	Leyland/DAB National Articulated	Leyland National Articulated B64T	South Yorkshire PTE	2006	A
C748 FFJ	1985	Ford Transit	Carlyle B16F	Devon General Omnibus & Touring Co	748	A

Notes:

UO 2331	Body new 1933		ADV 128	Rebodied 1950
VW 203	Body new 1936		AUO 74	Front end of chassis only
JY 124	New body and engine fitted in 1947		ETT 995	Rebuilt in 1953 using prewar mechanical components and rebodied
OD 7500	Rebodied 1949			
ATT 922	Rebodied in the late 1940s			

BOW 169	New with Beadle body; acquired by Wilts & Dorset Motor Services (505) in 1952 and converted to breakdown vehiclein 1956	EFJ 241	Converted to tree-cutter in 1958
		FTA 634	Damaged in 1941 by enemy action and rebuilt
		GTA 395	Lengthened and rebodied in 1954
EFJ 666	Used as a snow plough 1952-6	CTT 513C	Restored by the Oxford Bus Museum Trust
EUF 204	Rebodied 1949	CRM 927T	Articulated prototype (57 ft long)

A line-up of Winkleigh residents at last year's annual open day reveals West of England Transport Collection pioneer, Exeter 66, a 1938 Leyland TS8 with body by Cravens of Sheffield. Behind is 1934 Brush-bodied AEC Regent, Devon General DR213, another long-standing resident. *Philip Lamb*

Westgate Museum

Contact address: Enquiries: 14 Ilkley Road, Caversham, Reading RG4 7BD

Brief description: The collection, near Doncaster, is housed in a

former Methodist Chapel built in 1865. The vehicles operate at Sandtoft Transport Centre from time to time.

Opening days/times: Viewing strictly by appointment.

Registration	Date	Chassis	Body	New to	Fleet No	Status
RC 8472+	1944	Sunbeam W	Weymann UH30/26R	Derby Corporation	172	R
SVS 281	1945	Daimler CWA6	Duple UH30/26R	Douglas Corporation	52	R
DRD 130+	1949	BUT 9611T	Park Royal H33/26RD	Reading Corporation	144	R
LDP 945	1955	AEC Regent III 6812A	Park Royal L31/26RD	Reading Corporation	98	R
WLT 529	1960	AEC Routemaster R2RH	Park Royal H36/28R	London Transport	RM529	R
+ Trolleybus						

Notes:

SVS 281   Originally registered FMN 955.

Part 3
Heritage Buses Services

London Transport RF26 was the first 30ft x 7ft 6in RF. It was subsequently one of a number 'modified', somewhat of a cosmetic exercise, for continued Green Line service during the 1960s. Today it is part of the Memory Lane fleet, and can most Sundays be found working the 32 route between Guildford and Reigate via Dorking. *Philip Lamb*

Blue Triangle   Rainham

Contact address: Unit 3C, Denver Industrial Estate, Ferry Lane, Rainham, Essex, RM13 7MD.
Phone: 01708 631001

Operations planned for 2001: Scheduled heritage services not finalised at time of publication, but vehicles frequently appear on rail replacement services.

Registration	Date	Chassis	Body	New to	Fleet No	Status
HLW 178	1947	AEC Regent III O961	Weymann H30/26R	London Transport	RT191	
KGK 959	1949	AEC Regent III O961	Weymann H30/26R	London Transport	RT2150	
KXW 171	1950	AEC Regent III O961	Saunders H30/26R	London Transport	RT3062	
LLU 670	1950	AEC Regent III O961	Park Royal H30/26R	London Transport	RT3871	
LYR 969	1952	AEC Regent III O961	Weymann H30/26R	London Transport	RT2799	
MXX 289	1952	AEC Regal IV 9821LT	Metro-Cammell B39F	London Transport	RF401	
WLT 900	1961	AEC Routemaster R2RH/1	Park Royal H36/28R	London Transport	RML900	
CUV 260C	1965	AEC Routemaster R2RH/1	Park Royal H36/29RD	London Transport	RCL2260	

Blue Triangle maintains a number of former London Transport RTs including 1947 Weymann-bodied 'roofbox RT', RT191. *Nigel Appleford*

Carmel Coaches   Okehampton

Contact address: Mr A. G. Hazell, Northlew, Okehampton, Devon.
Phone: 01409 221237
Operations planned for 2001: Route 174:

Okehampton–Moretonhampstead (subject to confirmation from Devon CC).
Sundays and Bank Holidays, 27 May to 9 September.

Registration	Date	Chassis	Body	New to	Fleet No	Status
JFJ 875	1950	Daimler CVD6/SD	Weymann B35F	Exeter Corporation	75	
LOD 495	1950	Albion FT39N	Duple FC31F	Way & Son, Crediton		
MTT 640	1951	Leyland Titan PD2/1	Leyland L27/26R	Devon General Omnibus & Touring Co	DL644	

Notes:
MTT 640   Not licensed as PSV but likely to be used as publicity vehicle

Carmel Coaches of Okehampton, Devon regularly uses this 1950 Duple-bodied Albion Victor on its summer 174 service to Moretonhampstead, on behalf of Devon County Council. *John G. Lidstone*

Contact address: Cosy Coach Tours, 5 Meynell Way, Killamarsh, Derbyshire, S21 1HG.
Phone: 0114 248 9139
Operations planned for 2001: Sundays and Bank Holidays, 27 May to 27 August.
Bolsover Heritage Service: from Chesterfield station to Hardwicke Hall, then circular via Bolsover Castle, returning to Hardwicke Hall.
Fares: £5 for one complete circuit (with hop-on, hop-off facility);

£7.50 all-day ticket (unlimited travel).
Conections at Bolsover station with trains from Sheffield and Nottingham.
Comprehensive timetables are available from the above address for £1 plus SAE.
Pre-booked tickets are available from Tourist Information Office, Low Pavement, Chesterfield, Derbyshire.

Registration	Date	Chassis	Body	New to	Fleet No	Status
ATS 408	1948	Bedford OB	Duple C29F	James Meffan, Kirriemuir		
RBD 201	1961	Bristol MW6G	ECW C39F	United Counties Omnibus Co	201	

Notes:
RBD 201   Not yet operational at time of publication; may be used later in season.

Cosy Coaches of Killamarsh operates this Bedford OB on the Bolsover Heritage Service from Chesterfield station during the summer months. ATS 408 was new in 1948 and carries a Duple Vista body. *Tony Wilson*

Contact address: Bowber Head, Ravenstonedale, Kirkby Stephen, Cumbria, CA17 4NL.
Phone: 015396 23254
Website: www.cumbriaclassiccoaches.co.uk
E-mail: coaches@ cumbriaclassiccoaches.co.uk

Operations planned for 2001: Route 569: Ravenstonedale–Kirkby Stephen–Hawes, Tues (Hawes market day) May to September. Kendal Clipper (circular tour of Kendal), half-hourly, seven days a week during School Summer Holidays. Eden Valley heritage trip, Thurs June to September.

Registration	Date	Chassis	Body	New to	Fleet No	Status
WG 2373	1934	Leyland Lion LT5B	Burlingham B35F	W. Alexander & Sons	P169	
CRN 80	1949	Leyland Tiger PS1	East Lancs B34R	Preston Corporation	75	
CWG 286	1950	Leyland Tiger PS1/1	Alexander C35F	W. Alexander & Sons	PA184	

Notes:
WG 2373   Rebodied 1947

Cumbria Classic Coaches uses a number of half-cab saloons, including East Lancs-bodied Layland PS1 CRN 80, new in 1949 as Preston 75. *Tony Wilson*

Contact address: Warstone Motors Ltd, The Garage, Jacobs Hall Lane, Great Wyrley, Staffordshire WS6 6AD
Phone: 01922 414141

Operations planned for 2001: School Summer Holidays:
Route 5 (Cannock–Telford) Thurs
Route 14 (Cannock–Lichfield) Fri

Registration	Date	Chassis	Body	New to	Fleet No	Status
GZ 2248	1944	Bedford OWB	Duple B32F	Northern Ireland Road Transport Board		
GCA 747	1950	Bedford OB	Duple C29F	Owen, Rhostyllen		
GNY 432C	1965	Leyland Titan PD3/4	Massey L35/33RD	Caerphilly UDC	32	

Warstone Motors of Wyrley, trading as Green Bus Service, uses this recently restored 1944 Duple-bodied Bedford OWB on its Cannock-Lichfield service on Fridays during the summer. No 4 (GZ 2248) was new to the Northern Ireland Road Transport Board. *Tony Wilson*

Mac Tours   Edinburgh

Contact address: Edinburgh Vintage Bus Company, 11A James Court, Lawnmarket, Edinburgh EH1 2PB.
Phone: 0131 477 4771

Fax: 0131 220 0770
Operations planned for 2001: Hop-on, hop-off open-top tours of Edinburgh operate seven days a week, all year round.

Registration	Date	Chassis	Body	New to	Fleet No	Status
	1951	Leyland Tiger PS1	Guernseybus OB??F	Jersey Motor Transport Co	44	
	1951	Leyland Tiger PS1	Guernseybus B??F	Jersey Motor Transport Co	49	
833 AFM	1957	Bristol Lodekka LD6G	ECW O33/27RD	Crosville Motor Services	MG876	
LST 873	1958	Leyland Titan PD2/40	Park Royal O27/26RO	Barrow Corporation	165	
HSK 953	1959	Leyland Titan PD2/24	Alexander O29/28R	Glasgow Corporation	L108	
WUS 248	1959	AEC Reliance 2MU3RA	Plaxton C37F	Cotter's Motor Tours, Glasgow		
WLT 371	1960	AEC Routemaster R2RH	Park Royal H36/28R	London Transport	RM371	
XSL 228A	1961	Bristol Lodekka FS6G	ECW CO33/27RD	Bristol Omnibus Co	8576	
869 NHT	1961	Bristol Lodekka FS6G	ECW CO33/27RD	Bristol Omnibus Co	8579	
FTE 631B	1964	Leyland Titan PD3/4	East Lancs H41/32F	Rawtenstall Corporation	31	
CUV 203C	1965	AEC Routemaster R2RH	Park Royal H36/28R	London Transport	RM2203	
DHC 784E	1967	Leyland Titan PD2A/30	East Lancs O32/28R	Eastbourne Corporation	84	
HFR 507E	1967	Leyland Titan PD3A/1	Metro-Cammell H41/30R	Blackpool Corporation	507	
JTF 218F	1968	Leyland Titan PD2A/27	East Lancs O36/28F	Darwen Corporation	40	
WRH 294J	1970	Leyland Atlantean PDR1A/1	Roe O43/28F	Kingston-upon-Hull Corporation	294	
ARH 304K	1971	Leyland Atlantean PDR1A/1	Roe PO43/29F	Kingston-upon-Hull Corporation	304	

Notes:

[ex-JMT 44]	Originally registered J 5567, with Reading B34F body; new replica body built 1988/9
[ex-JMT 49]	Originally registered J 5660, with Reading B34F body; new replica body built 1990/1
833 AFM	Originally H33/27RD
LST 873	Originally H27/26R, registered CEO 952
HSK 953	Originally H29/28R, registered SGD 10
XSL 228A	Originally registered 866 NHT
DHC 784E	Originally H32/28R
JTF 218F	Originally H36/28F
WRH 294J	Originally H43/28F
ARH 304K	Originally H43/29F

The Mac Tours fleet is diverse and growing. Amongst its ranks is this former Hull Roe-bodied Leyland Atlantean WRH 294J, now a partially open topper.
Nigel Green

Contact address: 78 Lillibrooke Crescent, Maidenhead, Berkshire, SL6 3XQ.
Phone: 01628 825050
Fax: 01628 825851
E-mail: info@memorylane.co.uk

Operations planned for 2001: Route 32: Guildford–Redhill, Sundays and Bank Holidays all year round.

Registration	Date	Chassis	Body	New to	Fleet No	Status
KGU 290	1949	AEC Regent III O961	Weymann H30/26R	London Transport	RT1530	
KYY 628	1950	AEC Regent III O961	Park Royal H30/26R	London Transport	RT1790	
LYF 377	1951	AEC Regal IV 9821LT	Metro-Cammell B37F	London Transport	RF26	
MLL 943	1952	AEC Regal IV 9821LT	Metro-Cammell B39F	London Transport	RF525	
MLL 952	1952	AEC Regal IV 9821LT	Metro-Cammell B39F	London Transport	RF315	
NLE 643	1953	AEC Regal IV 9821LT	Metro-Cammell B39F	London Transport	RF643	
617 DDV	1960	Bristol MW6G	ECW C39F	Southern National Omnibus Co (Royal Blue)	2250	
253 KTA	1962	Bristol MW6G	ECW C39F	Western National Omnibus Co (Royal Blue)	2270	
618 WTE	1962	AEC Reliance 2MU3RA	Plaxton DP41F	Lancashire United Transport	94	
AFN 764B	1964	AEC Regent V 2D3RA	Park Royal O40/32F	East Kent Road Car Co		
TYD 122G	1969	AEC Reliance 6MU3R	Willowbrook B45F	Hutchings & Cornelius, South Petherton		
SFR 127J	1970	AEC Reliance 6U3ZR	Plaxton C53F	J. Abbott & Sons, Blackpool		
TCD 376J	1970	Daimler Fleetline CRG6LX	Northern Counties O40/31F	Southdown Motor Services	376	

Notes:
AFN 764B   Originally H40/32F
TCD 376J   Originally H40/31F

Former Southdown, Crosville and Northern Bus Northern Counties-bodied Daimler Fleetline TCD 376J is part of Memory Lane's private hire fleet. *Philip Lamb*

Contact address: Nostalgiabus Ltd, Unit 2, Riverside House, 43 Willow Lane, Mitcham, Surrey,
Phone: 0208 640 6668
Fax: 0208 395 4415

Operations planned for 2001:To be confirmed

Registration	Date	Chassis	Body	New to	Fleet No	Status
KYE 905	1950	Bedford OB	Duple C27F	Grey-Green Coaches, London		
MLL 523	1952	AEC Regal IV 9821LT	Metro-Cammell B39F	London Transport	RF136	
MXX 367	1954	Guy Special NLLVP	ECW B26F	London Transport	GS67	
YVS 288	1960	AEC Routemaster R2RH	Park Royal H36/28R	London Transport	RM357	
WFO 410	1960	AEC Routemaster R2RH	Park Royal H36/28R	London Transport	RM378	
394 CLT	1963	AEC Routemaster R2RH	Park Royal H36/28R	London Transport	RM1394	
571 CLT	1963	AEC Routemaster R2RH	Park Royal H36/28R	London Transport	RM1571	
CUV 156C	1965	AEC Routemaster R2RH	Park Royal H36/28R	London Transport	RM2156	
CUV 180C	1965	AEC Routemaster R2RH	Park Royal H36/28R	London Transport	RM2180	

Notes:
MLL 523	Prototype 'modernised' RF, rebuilt 1965
YVS 288	Originally registered WLT 357
WFO 410	Originally registered WLT 378

Formerly London Transport GS67, this ECW-bodied Guy Special is still earning its keep with Nostalgiabus as its No 7. *Julian Bowden*

Contact address: Station Works, Bishop's Lydeard, Somerset. TA4 3BU

Phone: 01823 433398

Operations planned for 2001: School Summer Holidays (days of operation vary — please check with the company for details):
Taunton Deane circular tour:
Bishop's Lydeard–Taunton–Hestercome Gardens–Fyne Court–Buncombe Hill–Kington St Mary, returning to Bishop's

Lydeard via Taunton station.
Also shuttle services between Taunton and Bishop's Lydeard in connection with the West Somerset Railway

Event attending: 4/5 August 2001 — Steam & Vintage Rally, Bishops Lydeard

Registration	Date	Chassis	Body	New to	Fleet No	Status
BTF 24	1937	Leyland Lion LT7c	Leyland B34R	Lytham St Annes Corporation	4	A
JG 9938	1937	Leyland Tiger TS8	Park Royal C32R	East Kent Road Car Co		R
AJA 132	1938	Bristol L5G	Burlingham B35R	North Western Road Car Co	372	R
HKL 819	1946	AEC Regal I O662	Beadle O35F	Maidstone & District Motor Services	OR1	R
HUO 510	1947	AEC Regal I O662	Weymann B35F	Devon General Omnibus & Touring Co	SR510	R
JUO 992	1947	Leyland Titan PD1	ECW L27/26R	Southern National Omnibus Co	2932	A
JFM 575	1948	AEC Regal III	Strachan B35R	Crosville Motor Services		RP
JUP 233	1948	AEC Regal III 6821A	Burlingham B35F	Gillet & Baker		R
JTE 546	1948	AEC Regent III 6811A	Park Royal H33/26R	Morecambe Heysham Corporation	20	R
KTF 594	1949	AEC Regent III 9621E	Park Royal O33/26R	Morecambe Heysham Corporation	65	R
CFN 121	1949	Dennis Lancet J3	Park Royal B35R	East Kent Road Car Co		R
LJH 665	1949	Dennis Lancet J3	Duple C35F	Lees, Barnet		RP
KFM 766	1950	Bristol L5G	ECW B35R	Crosville Motor Services	KG117	R
KFM 893	1950	Bristol L5G	ECW B35R	Crosville Motor Services	KG131	R
LFM 717	1950	Bristol L5G	ECW B35R	Crosville Motor Services	KG136	A
LFM 724	1950	Bristol L5G	ECW B35R	Crosville Motor Services	KG143	A
LFM 734	1950	Bristol LL5G	ECW B39R	Crosville Motor Services		R
CHL 772	1950	Daimler CVD6	Willowbrook DP35F	Bullock, Featherstone		R
GWN 432	1950	Dennis Lancet J3	Thurgood FC37F	Super, Tottenham		R
LFM 302	1950	Leyland Tiger PS1	Weymann B35R	Crosville Motor Services	KA226	R
FMO 949	1951	Bristol LL6B	ECW B39F	Thames Valley Traction Co	567	R
NLJ 271	1954	Leyland Royal Tiger PSU1/13	Burlingham B42F	Bournemouth Corporation	261	R
CHG 545	1954	Leyland Tiger PS2/14	East Lancashire Coachbuilders B39F	Burnley Colne & Nelson Joint Committee	45	R
200 APB	1956	AEC Reliance MU3RV	Burlingham B44F	Safeguard, Guildford		A
838 AFM	1957	Bristol Lodekka LD6G	ECW H33/27RD	Crosville Motor Services	MG881	R
VDV 752	1957	Bristol Lodekka LDL6G	ECW O37/33RD	Western National Omnibus Co	1935	R
VDV 753	1957	Bristol Lodekka LDL6G	ECW O37/33RD	Western National Omnibus Co	1936	R
SHO 800	1958	AEC Reliance MU2RA	Duple C43F	Creamline, Bordon		A
NDB 356	1958	Leyland Tiger Cub PSUC1/1	Crossley B44F	Stockport Corporation	403	R
890 ADV	1959	AEC Reliance 2MU3RV	Willowbrook C41F	Devon General Grey Cars	TCR890	RP
501 BTA	1959	Bristol Lodekka LD6G	ECW H33/27RD	Western National Omnibus Co	1949	A
503 BTA	1959	Bristol Lodekka LD6G	ECW H33/27RD	Western National Omnibus Co	1951	RP
120 JRB	1959	Daimler Freeline D650HS	Burlingham C37F	Tailby & George ('Blue Bus Services'), Willington		A
LDB 796	1960	Leyland Tiger Cub	Willowbrook DP43F	North Western Road Car Co		R
AFE 417A	1961	AEC Reliance	Weymann O40F	Maidstone & District Motor Services	S325	R
569 EFJ	1962	AEC Reliance 2MU4RA	Harrington C40F	Greenslades Tours, Exeter		A
CYD 724C	1965	AEC Reliance 2MU4RA	Harrington C41F	Hutchings & Cornelius Services, South Petherton		R
HJA 965E	1967	Leyland Titan PD2/40	East Lancashire Neepsend H36/28R	Stockport Corporation	65	R
FDG 468L	1973	AEC Reliance 6MU4R	Plaxton C45F	Cotterells, Mitcheldean		R

Rexquote Heritage operates services based on Taunton, and on Weston-super-Mare, where this 1957 Bristol LDL6G, formerly Western National 1936 is normally at work.
Philip Lamb

Southcoast Motor Services   Brighton

Contact address: PO Box 1029, Croydon CR9 6AA
Phone: 0890 321 5767
Website: www.southcoastmotorservices.co.uk
Operations planned for 2001: Route 77: Brighton (Palace Pier)–Devil's Dyke, Sundays and Bank Holidays Good Friday to October, plus Mon–Fri during School Summer Holidays and Saturdays in September and October.

Registration	Date	Chassis	Body	New to	Fleet No	Status
2722 CD	1961	Leyland Leopard L2	Harrington C41F	Southdown Motor Services	1722	
WRU 702B	1964	Leyland Titan PD3/4	Northern Counties FCO39/30F	Southdown Motor Services	406	
HCD 350E	1967	Leyland Titan PD3/4	Northern Counties FH39/30F	Southdown Motor Services	350	

Notes:

2722 CD	Originally C28F (2+1 seating)
WRU 702B	Originally registered 406 DCD

Indices

Stevensons 11, an all-Leyland 6RT was London
Transport RTW185. It is part of the RTW Bus Group
collection. *Philip Lamb*

Reg	Page	Reg	Page	Reg	Page	Reg	Page
1 RDV	106	326 CAA	85	569 EFJ	118	827 BWY	79
105 UTU	66	332 RJO	80	569 KKK	35	833 AFM	115
116 JTD	44	333 CRW	47	571 CLT	117	8340 U	85
116 TMD	92	334 CRW	21	574 CNW	84	838 AFM	118
120 JRB	118	335 AOW	99	574 TD	54	850 ABK	51
122 JTD	44	340 TJO	80	595 LCG	85	851 FNN	50
1252 EV	59	371 BKA	92	596 LCG	85	861 HAL	50
1294 RE	20	372 BKA	92			862 RAE	27
1322 WA	64	373 WPU	29	6162 RU	76	869 NHT	115
138 CLT	29	375 GWN	79	6167 RU	76	871 KHA	25
14 LFC	51	381 BKM	29	617 DDV	116	872 ATA	82
14 PKR	87	386 DD	101	618 WTE	116	875 VFM	92
1425 P	56	3916 UB	91	6219 TF	54	881 BTF	96
152 CLT	54	394 CLT	117	6220 KW	39	8859 VR	54
191 AWL	80	3945 UE	30	6249 UP	94	8860 VR	44
194 BFC	80			6314 HA	20	890 ADV	118
		404 RIU	67	6330 WJ	64	891 VFM	92
200 APB	118	414 CLT	44	6370 HA	21		
201 YTE	54	422 CAX	66	6545 HA	25	9 RDV	82
217 MHK	29	4227 FM	54	657 BWB	57	904 OFM	27
2206 OI	36	433 MDT	57	66	57	913 DTT	82
221 JVK	94	434 BTE	54	675 COD	79	918 NRT	29
236 LNO	29	436 KOV	21	6801 FN	35	924 AHY	84
248 NEA	25	453 AUP	54	694 ZO	67	931 GTA	82
253 KTA	116	462 EOT	72			932 GTA	82
256 SFM	92	4632 VM	44	70 AUF	99	935 GTA	82
264 ERY	21	488 KOT	72	72 MMJ	91	943 KHA	25
2722 CD	119			7209 PW	66	952 JUB	41
28 TKR	29	501 BTA	118	737 DYE	42	956 AJO	51
297 LJ	76	501 KD	92	7424 SP	60	960 HTT	82
		503 BTA	118	756 KFC	51	9629 WU	57
301 LJ	28	503 RUO	82	760 CTD	90	964 H87	56
3016 HA	25	504 EBL	48	7682 LJ	27	966 RVO	20
3035 HA	20	507 OHU	27	773 FHA	20	972 CUF	99
304 GHN	74	5073 HA	25	7874 WJ	64	974 AFJ	106
304 KFC	51	5228 NW	84			975 CWL	80
305 KFC	51	528 CTF	96	80 NVO	50	9797 DP	101
312 MFC	80	557 BNG	36	802 MHW	25	980 DAE	27
318 AOW	99	56 GUO	104	8154 EL	76	99-64-HB	25
3190 UN	101	561 TD	90	8156 EL	76	A706 LNC	46
324 NJO	80	562 RTF	54	8159 EL	76	A765 NNA	98

Reg	Page	Reg	Page	Reg	Page	Reg	Page
A927 MDV	104	AFT 930	94	AOG 679	20	AXJ 857	43
AAA 503C	72	AFY 971	52	AOL 17T	105	AXM 649	42
AAA 506C	72	AH 79505	36	APA 46B	50	AXM 693	32
AAA 508C	72	AHA 451J	64	APR 167A	50	AYV 651	42
AAA 756	58	AHA 582	22	APW 829B	37	AZD 203	30
AAL 522A	50	AHC 442	31	ARD 676	78	B106 XJO	51
ABR 433	93	AHE 163	41	ARG 17B	60	B259 MDL	38
AC-L 379	78	AHF 850	69	ARH 304K	115	B401 NJF	18
ACB 902	52	AHL 694	84	ARN 392	52	BBA 560	43
ACB 904	96	AHN 451B	74	ARN 658C	104	BBK 236B	31
ACC 88	52	AHU 803	77	ARN 811C	96	BCB 341	52
ACK 796	96	AHW 200V	27	ASC 665B	60	BCD 820L	48
ACU 304B	94	AJA 132	118	ATD 281J	90	BCK 367C	54
ACW 645	64	AJA 139B	54	ATD 683	52	BCK 939	56
AD 7156	51	AJA 152	43	ATF 477	58	BCP 671	91
ADV 128	106	AJA 408L	98	ATS 408	112	BCR 379K	99
ADX 1	37	AJX 369	91	ATT 922	106	BD 209	93
ADX 196	37	ALJ 340B	76	AUD 310J	80	BDJ 67	52
ADX 63B	37	ALJ 973	78	AUF 666	38	BDJ 808	52
AEK 514	39	ALJ 986	36	AUO 74	106	BDJ 87	57
AEL 170B	76	AML 582H	42	AUX 296	58	BDY 809	36
AFE 417A	118	AMS 513K	60	AVH 470	85	BED 731C	54
AFM 103G	54	ANA 551Y	55	AVX 975G	29	BEN 177	44
AFM 106G	54	ANB 851	20	AWA 124B	60	BFE 419	41
AFN 764B	116	ANO 395L	101	AWG 393	58	BFS 1L	60
AFN 780B	35	ANQ 778	52	AWG 623	58	BFS 463L	60

Reg	No	Reg	No	Reg	No	Reg	No
BG 8557	69	CDK 409C	91	DAU 370C	50	ECD 524	31
BG 9225	69	CDL 479C	38	DB 5070	43	ECU 201E	94
BHA 399C	25	CDR 679	58	DBA 214C	44	ECX 425	88
BHA 656C	25	CDT 636	56	DBE 187	41	ED 6141	52
BHL 682	84	CDX 516	32	DBN 978	66	EDB 549	44
BHO 670J	101	CET 613	56	DBU 246	52	EDB 562	44
BHU 92C	27	CFK 340	93	DCK 219	96	EDB 575	44
BJA 425	43	CFM 354	39	DCN 83	94	EDL 657	38
BK 2986	31	CFN 121	118	DCS 616	58	EDS 288A	59
BKC 236K	92	CFR 590C	54	DDB 174C	44	EDS 320A	59
BMS 222	59	CFV 851	28	DDM 652	20	EDS 50A	59
BMS 405	58	CGJ 188	32	DED 797	52	EDV 555D	79
BNC 960T	98	CHF 565	69	DEK 3D	102	EED 8	52
BND 874C	44	CHG 545	118	DEL 893C	79	EF 7380	93
BNE 729N	98	CHL 772	118	DFE 383	41	EFJ 241	106
BNE 751N	98	CJN 436C	99	DFE 963D	27	EFJ 666	106
BNE 764N	98	CK 3825	43	DFM 347H	55	EFJ 92	43
BOK 1V	25	CK 4518	93	DFV 146	90	EFN 591	35
BON 474C	25	CKG 193	78	DGS 536	58	EFV 300	88
BOW 162	76	CLE 122	42	DGS 625	59	EGA 79	47
BOW 169	106	CN 2870	22	DHC 784E	115	EGN 369J	32
BP 9822	18	CN 4740	93	DHD 177	39	EGO 426	32
BPV 10	37	CN 6100	93	DHN 475	84	EGP 1J	42
BPV 9	37	CNG 125C	37	DHR 192	48	EHA 415D	21
BR 7132	18	CNH 699	27	DHW 293K	78	EHA 424D	104
BRM 596	85	CNH 860	79	DJF 349	50	EHA 767D	25
BRS 37	58	CNH 862	79	DJP 754	44	EHA 775	20
BT 8939	93	CPM 61	48	DJY 965	106	EHL 336	84
BTF 24	118	CPU 979G	29	DKC 305L	55	EHL 344	84
BTF 25	106	CRC 911	66	DKT 11	39	EHL 472D	101
BTN 113	93	CRG 811	96	DKY 703	56	EHO 228	31
BTR 361B	99	CRM 927T	106	DKY 704	78	EHO 869	99
BUF 260C	99	CRN 80	113	DKY 706	56	EHV 65	31
BUF 277C	99	CRR 819	50	DKY 711	76	EKU 743	56
BUF 426C	99	CRS 834	96	DKY 712	76	EKU 746	56
BUS 181	87	CRU 103C	76	DKY 713	52	EKV 966	47
BWG 39	58	CRU 180C	76	DL 5084	38	EKY 558	56
BWG 833L	60	CRU 187C	76	DL 9015	38	ELP 228	32
BWO 585B	66	CSG 773S	62	DL 9706	102	EN 9965	98
BWS 105L	60	CSG 792S	62	DLJ 111L	76	END 832D	98
BXA452B	60	CTF 627B	90	DLJ 116L	76	ENW 980D	40
BXA 464B	60	CTP 200	31	DLJ 119L	76	EOD 524D	50
BXD 576	42	CTT 23C	82	DLU 92	32	EOI 4857	68
BXD 628	102	CTT 513C	106	DM 2583	93	ERD 152	56
C 2367	93	CTT 518C	50	DMS 820	58	ERN 700	96
C519 FFJ	83	CU 3593	78	DMS 823	58	ERU 159V	57
C526 DYT	43	CUH 856	39	DNF 204	66	ERV 247D	76
C729 JJO	80	CUL 260	36	DNF 708C	98	ERV 249D	76
C748 FFJ	106	CUS 297X	87	DOD 474	106	ERV 251D	76
C751 YBA	98	CUS 302X	87	DPT 848	93	ERV 252D	76
CAH 923	37	CUV 156C	117	DPV 68D	37	ERV 938	36
CAP 234	38	CUV 180C	117	DR 4902	48	ESF 647W	62
CBA 966L	85	CUV 203C	115	DRC 224	36	ESF 801C	60
CBC 921	18	CUV 208C	84	DRD 130	107	ESG 652	58
CBD 778K	25	CUV 219C	25	DRN 289	96	ETJ 108	58
CBR 539	94	CUV 229C	42	DRR 153B	99	ETO 452C	50
CBV 431	52	CUV 233C	29	DSD 936V	62	ETT 995	106
CC 1087	93	CUV 260C	110	DSG 169	58	EUD 256K	51
CC 7745	22	CVF 874	37	DTP 823	31	EUF 184	18
CC 8671	72	CVH 741	56	DU 4838	51	EUF 198	39
CC 9305	35	CVP 207	22	DUK 278	104	EUF 204	106
CC 9424	72	CWG 206	44	DUK 833	26	EUP 405B	94
CCG 296K	72	CWG 283	58	DWB 54H	64	EVA 324	58
CCG 704C	85	CWG 286	113	DWG 526	92	EVD 406	39
CCK 359	96	CWH 717	44	DWH 706W	98	EVL 549E	41
CCK 663	90	CWN 629C	27	DX 3988	37	EWM 358	52
CCX 777	85	CWU 146T	69	DX 5610	37	EWS 168D	60
CCX 801	85	CWX 671	39	DX 5629	37	EX 6644	52
CD 4867	18	CXX 171	32	DX 6591	37	EXV 201	36
CD 5125	18	CYD 724C	118	DX 7812	37	EXV 253	42
CDB 224	44	CYI 621	67	DX 8871	48	EZH 155	30
CDC 166K	101	CYJ 252	59	DY 5029	87	EZH 17	67
CDC 168K	101	CZ 7013	68	E815 WDV	83	EZH 231	67
CDH 501	20	D122 PTT	51	EA 4181	20	EZH 64	67
CDJ 878	54	D63 NOF	46	EBO 919	78	EZL 1	67

Reg	No.	Reg	No.	Reg	No.	Reg	No.
F685 YOG	21	FYS 988	47	GZ 1882	68	HWO 334	22
FAR 724K	101	FYS 996	87	GZ 2248	114	HWV 294	79
FBG 910	69	FYS 998	47	GZ 4696	68	HX 2756	42
FBN 232C	74	FYS 999	87	GZ 7638	66	HYM 768	42
FBR 53D	94	FZ 7883	68			HYM 812	78
FBU 827	52	FZ 7897	68	HA 3501	22	HZA 230	67
FC 2602	51			HA 4963	20	HZA 279	67
FCD 292D	99	GAA 580	72	HA 8047	51	HZD 593	67
FCD 294D	100	GAA 616	72	HAH 537L	79		
FCD 307D	100	GAJ 12	56	HAX 399N	27	IB 552	18
FCI 323	30	GAX 2C	79	HBF 679D	25	IF-14-62	28
FCK 844	96	GAY 171	18	HCD 350E	119	IIL 4595	60
FCK 884	96	GBJ 192	36	HCK 204G	54	IL 2849	68
FDG 468L	118	GBU 1V	98	HD 7905	64	ILI 98	30
FDL 927D	38	GCA 747	114	HDG 448	22	IY 1940	67
FDM 724	22	GCM 152E	69	HDJ 753	54	IY 7383	30
FDO 573	41	GDJ 435	54	HDK 835	44	IY 7384	67
FEA156	26	GDT 421	56	HDL 279	38	IY 8044	30
FEL 105L	77	GE 2446	58	HDV 639E	60		
FEL 751D	50	GEA 174	26	HE 12	93	J 1359	59
FES 831W	62	GEN 201	54	HEK 705	44	J 1418	51
FET 617	56	GFM 180C	92	HET 513	48	J 2503	49
FET 618	56	GFN 273	35	HF 9126	58	JA 7585	43
FFM 135C	54	GFN 546N	35	HFL 672L	21	JAA 708	85
FFM 136C	54	GFU 692	56	HFO 742	25	JAP 698	29
FFN 451	35	GFY 406	52	HFR 507E	115	JBN 153	44
FFU 860	41	GGA 670	58	HFR 512E	90	JC 5313	87
FFV 447D	60	GGG 300N	87	HFR 515E	90	JCK 530	96
FFY 401	52	GGR 103N	94	HG 9651	66	JCK 542	96
FFY 402	22	GHA 337	22	HGC 130	32	JCP 60F	48
FFY 403	52	GHA 415D	25	HGD 894L	87	JDJ 260K	55
FFY 404	52	GHD 765	64	HGM 335E	60	JDN 668	57
FHF 451	69	GHN 189	74	HGM 346E	60	JEL 257	27
FHF 456	54	GHN 574	56	HHA 637	22	JF 2378	20
FHN 833	41	GHT 154	77	HHN 202	93	JFJ 606	106
FHT 15D	27	GJ 2098	32	HHP 755	91	JFJ 875	111
FJJ 774	42	GJB 254	51	HJA 965E	118	JFM 575	118
FJW 616	22	GJB 279	69	HJY 296	106	JFM 650J	54
FJY 915E	76	GJG 751D	35	HKF 820	92	JG 8720	72
FKF 801D	92	GJX 331	39	HKL 819	118	JG 9938	118
FKF 835E	92	GK 3192	42	HKR 11	56	JHA 227L	101
FKF 933G	92	GK 5323	42	HKW 82	39	JHA 868E	25
FKU 758	57	GK 5486	42	HLJ 44	76	JHA 890	20
FLG 209V	77	GKD 434	92	HLW 159	52	JHL 708	84
FMO 949	118	GKE 68	104	HLW 178	110	JHL 983	84
FNC 304F	54	GKP 511	56	HLX 410	32	JHT 802	27
FNV 557	35	GLJ 957	106	HNB 24N	98	JKC 178	92
FON 630	20	GM 5875	69	HNW 131D	40	JKW 290W	25
FOP 429	28	GM 6384	59	HOD 30	39	JLJ 403	76
FPT 6G	96	GNC 276N	46	HOR 493	85	JMA 413L	55
FR 1347	48	GNF 15V	98	HOR 590E	85	JMC 121K	18
FRB 211H	25	GNM 235N	106	HOR 592E	85	JMN 727	56
FRC 956	22	GNU 569N	25	HOU 904	72	JMY 120N	25
FRJ 254D	44	GNY 432C	114	HOV 685	22	JN 5783	48
FRJ 511	66	GO 5198	42	HPW 108	79	JNA 467	44
FRU 305	66	GOG 214W	105	HPW 133	41	JNB 416	47
FSC 182	58	GOU 732	104	HRN 249G	96	JND 629	52
FSU 102T	87	GOU 845	72	HRN 39	96	JND 646	44
FTA 634	106	GRS 343E	60	HSC 173X	62	JND 728	66
FTB 11	52	GRY 60D	25	HSK 953	115	JND 791	44
FTE 631B	115	GSC 658X	62	HTB 656	43	JNK 681C	91
FTO 614	56	GSC 667X	62	HTF 586	43	JO 5403	51
FTT 704	77	GTA 395	106	HTF 644B	54	JOJ 222	20
FVH 1	85	GTP 175F	99	HTJ 521B	54	JOJ 245	22
FW 5698	41	GTV 666	56	HTT 487	82	JOJ 257	20
FW 8990	56	GTX 761W	50	HUD 476S	51	JOJ 526	20
FWG 846	59	GUE 247	22	HUO 510	118	JOJ 533	22
FWL 371E	51	GUJ 608	20	HUP 236	93	JOJ 548	20
FWW 596	39	GUP 907N	94	HUS 675	87	JOJ 707	20
FWX 914	39	GUX 188	67	HUS 676	87	JOJ 847	20
FXH 521	36	GVD 47	58	HVH 234	85	JOJ 976	22
FXT 122	102	GW 713	48	HVH 472D	88	JOV 613P	25
FYG 663J	101	GWJ 724	64	HVM 901F	44	JOV 714P	21
FYS 839	78	GWN 432	118	HVU 244N	46	JOW 499E	99
		GYC 160K	27	HW 6634	27	JP 4712	43

Reg	No.	Reg	No.	Reg	No.	Reg	No.
JPA 190K	32	KHA 352	20	LFM 717	118	MDL 880R	38
JPT 544	93	KHC 369	57	LFM 724	118	MDT 222	57
JRJ 268E	35	KHL 855	84	LFM 734	118	MFR 306P	96
JRJ 281E	44	KHU 326P	27	LFM 753	27	MGE 183P	64
JRN 41	96	KHW 306E	25	LFM 756	92	MHU 49	27
JRR 404	22	KHW 630	27	LFR 529F	54	MHY 765	64
JRR 930	50	KHY 383	35	LFS 296F	100	MJ 4549	72
JRT 82K	37	KIJ 4035	68	LFS 480	59	MJA 891G	44
JSC 900E	60	KJ 2578	52	LFW 326	41	MJA 897G	44
JSF 928T	62	KJA 299G	54	LG 2637	66	MJD 759	94
JSX 595T	62	KJA 871F	44	LHA 870F	21	MKB 994	92
JT 8077	38	KJD 401P	42	LHL 164F	84	MLL 523	117
JTA 314	106	KLB 716	102	LHN 784	56	MLL 584	20
JTD 300B	54	KLB 908	97	LHN 860	74	MLL 685	32
JTE 546	118	KLB 915	97	LHT 911	89	MLL 740	32
JTF 218F	115	KLJ 346	76	LHW 918	27	MLL 817	102
JTF 920B	57	KMN 519	92	LHY 937	28	MLL 943	116
JUB 29	91	KNG 374	37	LIL 9929	62	MLL 952	116
JUE 349	22	KNV 337	79	LJ 500	76	MLL 969	32
JUO 992	118	KOD 585	82	LJ 9501	32	MMN 302	92
JUP 233	118	KOM 150	47	LJH 665	118	MMW 354G	79
JV 9901	56	KON 311P	25	LJX 198	91	MN 2615	42
JVH 381	39	KOU 791P	27	LJX 215	91	MNW 86	39
JVO 230	50	KOW 910F	99	LLU 613	20	MO 9324	18
JVU 775	44	KOX 663F	21	LLU 670	110	MOD 978	76
JVW 430	28	KOX 780F	25	LLU 829	36	MOF 90	20
JWB 416	64	KPM 91E	60	LLU 957	97	MOR 581	72
JWS 594	58	KPT 909	48	LLU 987	97	MPU 21	79
JWU 244N	88	KR 1728	52	LMA 284	44	MPU 52	28
JWU 886	39	KRN 422	54	LMJ 653G	48	MRT 6P	37
JWV 275W	31	KRU 55F	76	LN 4743	36	MSD 407	54
JWW 375	56	KSK 270	57	LN 7270	93	MSF 750P	60
JWW 376	56	KTC 615	52	LNA 166G	98	MTB 848	44
JWW 377	56	KTD 768	52	LNN 89E	50	MTC 540	96
JX 7046	91	KTF 589	58	LOD 495	111	MTE 639	58
JX 9106	91	KTF 594	118	LOG 301	20	MTL 750	18
JXC 288	32	KTT 689	20	LOG 302	20	MTT 640	111
JXC 432	22	KTV 493	56	LOU 48	72	MTT 640	82
JXN 370	91	KTV 506	56	LPT 328	94	MUA 45P	40
JY 124	106	KUF 199F	100	LRN 321J	96	MUA 865P	84
		KUO 972	106	LRN 60J	27	MUA 870P	40
KAG 856	39	KUS 607E	74	LRV 996	31	MXX 23	22
KAH 407	37	KVF 247V	25	LSC 936T	62	MXX 289	110
KAH 408	36	KVH 219	57	LST 873	115	MXX 332	102
KAL 579	22	KVH 473E	40	LTA 772	48	MXX 334	32
KBD 712D	102	KVO 429P	50	LTA 813	104	MXX 364	42
KBD 714D	60	KW 1961	36	LTB 907	41	MXX 367	117
KBO 961	78	KW 2260	39	LTC 774	44	MXX 410	102
KCK 869	96	KW 474	41	LTE 489P	55	MXX 430	102
KCK 914	96	KW 7604	41	LTF 254	91	MXX 434	102
KD 3185	87	KWE 255	64	LTN 501	49	MXX 489	102
KDB 408F	44	KWT 642D	40	LTU 869	67	MYA 590	32
KDJ 999	54	KXW 171	110	LUC 210	32	MZ 7396	67
KDL 885F	38	KXW 488	35	LUO 47F	82		
KDT 206D	57	KYE 905	117	LUO 595	106	N 7588	96
KDT 393	56	KYY 622	102	LUS 524E	60	NAC 416F	51
KED 546F	89	KYY 628	116	LVK 123	93	NAE 3	79
KEL 110	76	KYY 653	28	LWB 383P	64	NAG 120G	60
KEL 127	76	KYY 872	35	LWB 388P	64	NAT 766A	64
KEL 131	20			LWR 424	39	NBB 628	36
KEL 133	76	LA 9928	42	LYF 377	116	NBN 436	74
KET 220	64	LAA 231	72	LYR 533	39	NBU 494	44
KFF 367	69	LAE 13	77	LYR 826	32	NCK 338J	96
KFM 766	118	LAK 309G	40	LYR 910	32	NCS 16P	60
KFM 775	22	LC 3701	42	LYR 915	102	NDB 356	118
KFM 893	118	LCD 52	36	LYR 969	110	NDH 959	78
KGK 529	97	LDB 796	118	LYR 997	28	NDK 980	44
KGK 575	97	LDJ 985	54			NDL 656R	60
KGK 803	32	LDN 96	54	MAF 544	106	NDL 769G	74
KGK 959	110	LDP 945	107	MAH 744	37	NDV 537G	82
KGM 664F	60	LDS 201A	60	MAL 310	50	NEA 101F	25
KGU 290	116	LED 71P	55	MCK 229J	84	NEH 453	28
KGU 413	28	LEN 101	84	MCN 30K	94	NFM 67	27
KGY 4D	42	LF 9967	93	MDJ 554E	54	NFS 176Y	62
KHA 301	104	LFM 302	118	MDJ 555E	54	NG 1109	38

NHA 744	22	OHY 938	27	POU 494	85	RV 4649	31
NHA 795	22	OJ 9347	20	PRN 145	96	RV 6360	52
NHN 128	39	OJD 903R	25	PRN 79K	96	RV 6368	31
NHU 2	84	OJO 727	80	PRN 906	96	RWB 87	64
NJA 568W	98	OKW 515R	64	PRX 190B	99		
NJO 703	51	OLD 589	42	PRX 200B	99	SB 8155	20
NJW 719E	25	OLD 714	41	PRX 206B	31	SBN 767	74
NKD 536	92	OLD 717	29	PSJ 480	54	SCD 731N	100
NKD 540	92	OLJ 291	48	PSJ 825R	64	SCH 117X	50
NKT 896	35	ONE 744	54	PTC 114C	44	SCH 237	26
NLE 534	32	ONF 865H	98	PTE 944C	44	SCS 333M	60
NLE 537	42	ONO 49	28	PTW 110	28	SCS 366M	60
NLE 643	116	ONO 59	41	PUF 165H	100	SDA 757S	105
NLE 672	32	OOX 816R	21	PUH 149W	40	SDL 268	38
NLE 939	102	OP 237	20	PUO 331M	27	SDX 57	29
NLJ 268	76	OPN 807	79	PV 817	37	SFC 609	51
NLJ 271	118	ORB 277	22	PV 8270	37	SFC 610	51
NLJ 272	76	ORC 545P	50	PV 9371	37	SFR 127J	116
NLP 645	48	ORJ 83W	46	PVH 931	78	SFV 421	96
NMA 328D	66	ORS 60R	60	PW 8605	93	SG 2030	36
NMN 907	92	ORU 230G	76	PWL 413	51	SGD 239	87
NMR 345	76	ORV 989	31	PWL 999W	80	SGD 241	87
NMY 634E	60	OSJ 629R	60			SGD 407	29
NNB 125	44	OT 8283	72	Q507 OHR	27	SGD 448	87
NNB 547H	98	OT 8592	72			SGD 491	87
NNB 589H	98	OT 8898	72	RAG 411	59	SGD 500	87
NNC 855P	96	OTA 632G	25	RAG 578	59	SGD 65	87
NNN 968	50	OTA 640G	104	RAR 690J	101	SGF 483L	79
NNU 123M	80	OTT 43	104	RB 4757	87	SHA 431	22
NNU 124M	80	OTT 55	48	RBD 201	112	SHA 645G	25
NNU 234	76	OTV 137	57	RBW 87M	80	SHN 301	94
NNW 492	39	OTV 161	50	RC 2721	41	SHO 800	118
NOB 413M	104	OU 1805	72	RC 4615	22	SJ 1340	58
NOC 600R	104	OU 9286	85	RC 8472+	107	SKB 168	92
NOE 544R	25	OUM 727P	18	SVS 281	107	SKB 224	92
NOV 880G	104	OV 4090	22	RC 8575	56	SKB 695G	92
NPD 127L	102	OV 4486	22	RCB 345G	101	SLT 56	42
NRN 586	96	OVL 473	102	RCH 518F	50	SLT 57	42
NSJ 502	60	OW 928	99	RCM 493	69	SLT 58	32
NTF 466	54	OWC 182D	79	RCP 237	39	SMS 120P	60
NTT 661	82	OWE 116	64	RCS 382	60	SO 3740	58
NTT 679	82	OWE 271K	25	RCU 838S	94	SOA 674S	102
NTW 942C	29	OWJ 353A	54	RD 111	72	SOE 913H	104
NTY 416F	60	OWS 620	59	RD 7127	78	SOU 456	72
NUB 609	39	OWT 776M	40	RDB 872	27	SOU 465	72
NUD 105L	80	OWY 750K	40	RDH 505	22	SPK 203M	32
NUW 567Y	42	OZ 6686	67	RDS 597W	87	SPT 65	94
NVK 341	94			RDV 423H	27	SRB 424	47
NWU 265D	40	PBC 734	47	REN 116	44	SRJ 328H	55
NXP 506	59	PBN 668	54	RFE 416	41	SS 7486	58
NXP 997	42	PCG 888G	99	RFM 408	79	SS 7501	58
NZE 598	67	PCG 889G	99	RFM 641	69	SSC 212P	60
NZE 620	67	PCN 762	94	RFM 644	54	SSX 602V	62
NZE 629	67	PCW 203J	94	RFU 689	79	STO 523H	50
		PDH 808	22	RHS 400W	62	SUK 3	22
O 9926	22	PDJ 269L	55	RKC 262	92	SVS 904	39
OAX 9F	79	PDL 515	38	RN 7824	43	SWS 671	59
OBN 502R	98	PDL 519	38	RN 8622	39	SWS 715	59
OC 527	22	PDU 125M	47	RNA 220J	98	SXA 63K	60
OCK 985K	36	PFN 858	64	RNA 236J	101	SYG 561	39
OCO 502	106	PFN 865	50	ROD 765	91	SYX 569F	100
OD 5868	106	PFR 346	54	RRN 405	90		
OD 7497	82	PFR 554H	90	RRN 428	96	TBC 164	18
OD 7500	106	PGK 872	39	RRS 46R	60	TBK 190K	31
ODE 182	88	PHA 370M	25	RRU 901	76	TCD 374J	100
ODL 399	38	PHJ 953	35	RRU 903	20	TCD 376J	116
ODL 400	38	PHJ 954	29	RRU 904	76	TCD 383J	100
OED 217	28	PHN 699	94	RSK 615	20	TCD 490J	100
OFC 205	51	PJX 232	39	RTC 645L	55	TCH 274L	25
OFC 393	51	PJX 35	84	RTJ 422L	90	TCK 465	96
OFC 902H	80	PJX 43	39	RTT 996	27	TCK 726	96
OFM 957K	69	PND 460	44	RU 2266	76	TDH 912	26
OFS 777	59	PNF 941J	98	RU 8678	58	TDH 914	57
OFS 798	59	PNU 114K	80	RUF 37R	100	TDJ 612	54
OHK 432	41	POR 428	72	RV 3411	31	TDK 322	64

TDL 126S	38	ULS 717X	62	VY 957	43	XLS 945A	59
TDL 567K	84	UMA 370	44	VZI 44	67	XM 7399	42
TDL 998	38	UMP 227	32	VZL 179	67	XMS 252R	60
TE 5110	66	UO 2331	106	W 963	50	XNG 770S	37
TE 5780	87	UOU 417H	85	WAJ 112	59	XON 41J	21
TE 7870	72	UOU 419H	85	WBR 246	39	XRU 277K	76
TE 8318	41	UP 551	49	WBR 248	94	XSL 228A	115
TET 135	64	UTC 672	44	WCG 104	85	XSN 25A	59
TF 6860	39	UTN 501Y	94	WDA 700T	21	XTA 839	82
TF 818	41	UTU 596J	25	WDA 835T	105	XTC 684	28
TFJ 808	106	UU 6646	32	WDA 956T	105	XTF 98D	54
TGM 214J	60	UUA 214	39	WDA 986T	105	XU 7498	93
THL 261H	84	UUF 516J	100	WDF 569	25	XUF 141	99
TJ 836	72	UWX 981F	101	WEX 685M	84	XUO 721	82
TJO 56K	80	UXD 129G	102	WFM 801K	40	XVU 341M	98
TMS 585H	60	UZG 100	67	WFN 513	35	XVU 352M	46
TNA 496	44			WFO 410	117	XVU 363M	98
TNA 520	44	VBA 151S	55	WG 2373	113	XVX 19	29
TNB 759K	98	VBD 310H	101	WG 3260	58	XWX 795	57
TOB 997H	104	VD 3433	58	WG 8107	58	XX 9591	32
TRJ 109	54	VDL 264K	38	WG 8790	58		
TRJ 112	44	VDV 752	118	WG 9180	64	YDB 453L	98
TRN 731	39	VDV 753	118	WH 1553	41	YDK 590	44
TTA 400H	99	VDV 760	64	WHL 970	84	YDL 135T	38
TTD 386H	44	VDV 798	82	WHN 411G	94	YDL 318	38
TTT 781	82	VDV 817	82	WLT 371	115	YDW 756K	85
TUO 217J	104	VER 262L	51	WLT 506	20	YFR 351	90
TUO 497	79	VF 2788	37	WLT 529	107	YG 7831	93
TUO 74J	82	VF 8157	93	WLT 759	87	YHT 958	27
TUP 329R	94	VFU 864J	60	WLT 900	110	YHY 80	77
TUP 859	94	VG 5541	104	WLT 991	54	YLG 717F	40
TV 9333	56	VH 2088	87	WNG 864H	25	YLJ 147	76
TWH 809K	74	VH 6188	76	WNL 259A	94	YLJ 286	36
TWL 928	51	VH 6217	76	WNO 478	28	YNX 478	51
TWS 910T	27	VJO 201X	80	WRA 12	64	YOX 133K	104
TWT 123	84	VK 5401	49	WRH 294J	115	YPT 796	94
TWW 766F	40	VKB 711	92	WRU 702B	119	YR 3844	42
TWY 8	84	VKB 841	92	WT 7101	39	YRC 194	50
TXJ 507K	44	VKB 900	92	WT 7108	49	YRT 898H	36
TY 9608	84	VL 1263	41	WT 9156	87	YSD 350L	60
TYD 122G	116	VLT 140	48	WTE 155D	60	YSG 101	60
TYD 888	59	VM 4439	43	WTS 429A	99	YTE 826	36
		VML 5G	87	WUS 288	115	YVS 288	117
UCS 659	60	VMP 10G	60	WV 1209	37	YWL 134K	80
UCX 275	59	VMP 8G	60	WW 4688	78	YYB 239H	101
UDT 455F	57	VNB 101L	44	WWH 43L	98	YYJ 914	60
UF 1517	18	VNB 177L	98	WWJ 754M	57		
UF 6473	18	VNB 203L	98	WWY 115G	101	ZC 714	66
UF 6805	18	VO 6806	48	WYJ 813	35	ZD 7163	67
UF 7428	18	VO 8846	50	WZJ 724	67	ZD 726	68
UFC 430K	51	VOD 107S	83			ZH 3926	67
UFJ 292	94	VOD 550K	82	XAK 355L	40	ZH 3937	67
UFJ 296	82	VPT 598R	94	XBU 1S	98	ZH 4538	67
UFM 52F	69	VR 5742	43	XC 8059	42	ZI 9708	66
UGB 193W	87	VRC 612Y	50	XCW 955R	96	ZJ 5904	30
UGB 196W	87	VRD 193	57	XDH 516G	25	ZJ 5933	67
UHA 255	22	VRF 372	28	XDH 519G	26	ZL 2718	67
UHA 956H	25	VRU 124J	76	XDH 56G	25	ZL 6816	67
UHA 969H	21	VSC 86	59	XDH 72	78	ZO 6819	67
UHA 981H	25	VSF 542V	62	XEM 898W	69	ZO 6857	67
UHJ 842	29	VTU 76	39	XFM 42G	60	ZO 6881	67
UHY 359	27	VUD 30X	80	XG 9304	58	ZO 6949	67
UHY 362	104	VUD 348H	80	XGA 8J	87	ZO 6960	30
UI 8511	67	VUP 328	94	XHA 482	22	ZU 9241	67
UK 9978	26	VV 5696	79	XHA 496	22	ZV 1465	99
UKA 562H	92	VV 9135	58	XHO 370	72	ZY 79	67
UKE 830X	51	VVF 543	79	XJA 534L	98	ZY1715	30
UL 1771	28	VVP 911	25	XKC 862K	92		
ULS 716X	62	VW 203	106	XLG 477	39		

Index of Museums, Collections and Heritage Bus Services

Abbey Pumping Station, Leicester. 18
Aldershot & District Bus Interest Group 72
Amberley Museum. 18
Aston Manor Road Transport Museum, Aston 20
Aston, Aston Manor Road Transport Museum 20
Aycliffe & District Bus Preservation Society 74
Beamish, North of England Open Air Museum. 49
Birkenhead, Wirral Transport Museum. 69
Birmingham & Midland Museum of Transport,
   Wythall 22
Black Country Living Museum, Dudley 26
Blue Triangle, Rainham* 118
Bolton Bus Group 74
Bournemouth Heritage Transport Collection 76
Bristol Aero Collection, Kemble 27
Bristol Vintage Bus Group. 77
British Commercial Vehicle Museum, Leyland 28
British Trolleybus Society 78
Canvey Island, Castle Point Transport Museum. 29
Cardiff & South Wales Trolleybus Project 78
Carlton Colville, East Anglia Transport Museum, ... 35
Carmel Coaches, Okehampton* 110
Castle Point Transport Museum, Canvey Island. 28
Cavan & Leitrim Railway, Dromod. 30
Cheetham, Manchester Museum of Transport 43
Chelveston Preservation Society. 78
Chesterfield 123 Group. 80
Cherwell Bus Preservation Group 80
City of Portsmouth Preserved Transport Depot,
   Portsmouth 30
Cobham Bus Museum 32
Cosy Coaches, Killamarsh* 112
Covent Garden, London Transport Museum 42
Coventry, Museum of British Road Transport 47
Cultra, Ulster Folk & Transport Museum 68
Cumbria Classic Coaches, Kirkby Stephen*. 113
Devon General Society. 82
Dewsbury Bus Museum 84
Dover Transport Museum, Whitfield. 35
Dromod, Cavan & Leitrim Railway. 30
Dudley, Black Country Living Museum, ... 26
East Anglia Transport Museum, Carlton Colville. 35
East Pennine Transport Group 85
Edinburgh, Mac Tours* 115
Friends of King Alfred Buses 85
Glasgow Bus Museum 87
Glasgow, Museum of Transport. 47
Golcar Transport Collection. 87
Great Wyrley, Green Bus Service*. 114
Green Bus Service, Great Wyrley*. 114
Howth, Transport Museum Society of Ireland. 66
Huddersfield Passenger Transport Group 88
Imperial War Museum, London 36
Ipswich Transport Museum 37
Isle of Wight Bus Museum, Newport (IoW) 38
Keighley Bus Museum, Denholme. 39
Kirkby Stephen, Cumbria Classic Coaches*. 113
Kelvin Amos Collection 89
Kemble, Bristol Aero Collection 27
Killamarsh, Cosy Coaches* 112
Lancastrian Transport Trust. 90
Lathalmond, Scottish Vintage Bus Museum. 58
Legionnaire Group 91
Leicester, Abbey Pumping Station. 18

Leyland, British Commercial Vehicle Museum 28
Lincolnshire Road Transport Museum,
   North Hykeham 41
London, Imperial War Museum 36
London Transport Museum, Covent Garden 42
Long Hanborough, Oxford Bus Museum 51
Mac Tours, Edinburgh* 115
Maidenhead, Memory Lane Travel* 116
Manchester Museum of Transport, Cheetham 43
Meltham Mills Bus Museum 91
Memory Lane Travel, Maidenhead* 116
Merseyside Transport Trust. 92
Mike Sutcliffe Collection 93
Mitcham, Nostalgiabus*. 116
Mossley, Tameside Transport Collection 66
Museum of British Road Transport, Coventry. 47
Museum of Transport, Glasgow. 47
National Museum of Science and Industry,
   Wroughton. 48
Newport (IoW), Isle of Wight Bus Museum 38
North East Bus Preservation Society. 93
North Hykeham, Lincolnshire Road Transport
   Museum, ... 41
North of England Open Air Museum, Beamish. 49
Nottingham Transport Heritage Centre,
   Ruddington 50
Nostalgiabus, Mitcham*. 116
Okehampton, Carmel Coaches* 110
Oxford Bus Museum, Long Hanborough 51
Portsmouth, City of Portsmouth Preserved
   Transport Depot. 30
Rainham, Blue Triangle* 118
Rexquote Heritage, Wiveliscombe* 118
Ribble Vehicle Preservation Trust 96
RTW Bus Group 97
Ruddington, Nottingham Transport Heritage
   Centre. 50
Sandtoft Transport Centre. 56
Scottish Vintage Bus Museum, Lathalmond 58
SELNEC Preservation Society. 98
Sheffield Bus Museum, Tinsley 64
Solent Transport Trust 99
South Coast Motor Services*. 119
Southdown Historic Vehicle Group 99
St Helens Transport Museum 52
Tameside Transport Collection, Mossley 66
Telford Bus Group. 101
Three Counties Bus and Commercial Vehicle Museum 102
Tinsley, Sheffield Bus Museum 64
Transport Museum Society of Ireland, Howth 66
Ulster Folk & Transport Museum, Cultra 68
Wealdstone & District Vintage Vehicle Collection. 102
West Country Historic Omnibus & Transport Trust. 104
West Midlands Bus Preservation Society. 104
West of England Transport Collection 106
Westgate Museum 115
Whitfield, Dover Transport Museum. 35
Wirral Transport Museum, Birkenhead. 69
Wiveliscombe, Rexquote Heritage* 118
Wroughton, National Museum of Science &
   Industry. 48
Wythall, Birmingham & Midland Museum of
   Transport. 22

* Operators of Heritage Bus Seevices